Physiology of reproduction

PHYSIOLOGY OF REPRODUCTION

WILLIAM D. ODELL, M.D., Ph.D.

Chief, Division of Endocrinology, Harbor General Hospital,
Torrance, California; Professor of Medicine and Physiology, School of
Medicine, University of California at Los Angeles

DEAN L. MOYER, M.D.

Professor of Obstetrics, Gynecology, Pathology and Chief,
Section of Experimental Pathology, University of Southern California School of
Medicine, Los Angeles

With 104 illustrations

THE C. V. MOSBY COMPANY

Saint Louis   1971

PREFACE

The number of humans living on earth is presently doubling each thirty years. This doubling rate has progressively decreased in time interval required, from about two hundred years in the 1600s, to one hundred years in the 1800s and to fifty years in the mid-1900s. Thus growth of the human population has followed, without major deviations, the same growth curves observed for populations of microorganisms cultured in the laboratory. Extensive investigations directed toward improving efficiency of obtaining food supplies (the essentials) and "luxuries" that are necessary for some form of dignified life are presently under way along technical, political, and sociological lines. We are far from achieving success, particularly in the areas of politics and sociology; however, it appears that, in addition to success in these endeavors, some form of worldwide population control must be achieved. At present in Latin America population growth is so high that the bulk of local economic growth and economic assistance supplied from other countries is used just to maintain existing standards of living. Few funds are available to decrease illiteracy, improve health, and provide education and homes. Reproductive physiologists are actively seeking effective means of contraception. Information concerning reproduction is rapidly accumulating and concepts are constantly changing.

This book offers current concepts of basic reproductive processes in the human. It is not intended as a text on clinical medicine or pathology, and no reference to important disease states is included. Instead it presents in a succinct manner an integrated summation of data presently available in the literature and our own concepts of human reproductive physiology. We trace reproductive processes first through what we have termed a *static view* of the systems involved and then second through a *dynamic view*. We include maturation of the system components and of the integrated system (puberty), the functioning systems in males and females, conception and the steps through early uterine implantation. We do not include discussions of pregnancy, parturition, or postpartum states and their physiology. These subjects would require an additional text. When human data are limited, we draw upon animal studies and attempt to point out possible relationship to the human. It is our hope that this text will serve to prepare a solid base from which the budding reproductive physiologist can launch himself into an investigative career.

Much of the data presented in this book was unpublished at the time these chapters were written. Without the assistance of good friends and permission to draw generously from their investigations and thoughts during formation, this writing would not have been possible. Some of these same investigators were kind enough to read selected chapters and make helpful suggestions to improve their presentation. Many pleasant hours of discussion were spent in clarifying some of the concepts

PREFACE

presented. For all these reasons we happily express our thanks and gratitude. We particularly wish to thank Drs. Robert Blizzard, Richard Horton, Griff Ross, Ronald Swerdloff, Delbert Fisher, Stanley Korenman, Guy Abraham, David Solomon, Bernard Gondos, Robert Sparkes, and Mario Stefanini.

Preparation of the manuscript was accomplished almost solely through the voluntary efforts of Mrs. Beverly Fisher and Mrs. Marilyn Hescox. They spent many hours, frequently during evenings and holidays, proofreading, editing, and typing.

Last, as other endeavors undertaken in addition to regular working activities have done, this text required both of us to give to it many hours during evenings and holidays. We thank our wives and children for their patience, understanding, and assistance during these times.

William D. Odell
Dean L. Moyer

CONTENTS

Hormone measurement

The processes of reproduction are controlled by a number of hormones that circulate in blood in very small amounts, often making their identification and quantification difficult. Table 1-1 lists some of the hormones concerned with reproduction and their approximate molar concentration in blood from men and women. Within the ranges listed are encompassed all the important physiological changes discussed later.

To understand and interpret the accumulating knowledge about reproduction, one must have some familiarity with the adequacy and the inadequacies of methods of hormone measurement. The hormones we are concerned with are of two general types: polypeptide hormones and steroid hormones. Three methods of hormone measurement are used: (1) chemical assay, (2) bioassay, and (3) competitive binding assay. The general principles of each are presented, along with one or two specific examples and problems of specificity, precision, and sensitivity. The terms "precision," "specificity," and "sensitivity" apply to all three of the hormone measurement systems and should be understood by the reader. *Precision* is the accuracy or reliability with which one can define the potency or hormonal content of any material.* *Sensitivity* is the minimal detectable dose of hormone required to produce a response significantly different from zero. *Specificity* is the degree to which the response is characteristic of the hormone in question. Some assays respond to several hormones and are nonspecific. Fig. 1-1 depicts a semilog plot of a generalized dose response curve and would be applicable to any assay system—chemical, biological, or immunological. On such a plot there is an area below the minimum

Table 1-1. Concentration of some hormones controlling processes of reproduction

Hormone	Average molar concentration in blood (M/L)
Estradiol*	1 to 10 $\times 10^{-11}$
Luteinizing (interstitial cell–stimulating)	1 to 6 $\times 10^{-11}$
Follicle-stimulating	1 to 6 $\times 10^{-11}$
Testosterone*	1 to 20 $\times 10^{-10}$
Progesterone*	3 to 300 $\times 10^{-10}$
Thyroxine* (total)	1 $\times 10^{-7}$
Free thyroxine	2 to 6 $\times 10^{-11}$
Cortisol*	3 to 20 $\times 10^{-7}$
Free cortisol	6 $\times 10^{-9}$

*These hormones circulate bound to binding proteins. The concentration of free or unbound hormones is less. The ranges given for progesterone and estradiol concentrations include those in men and in women.

---

*The precision of an assay with a linear dose response curve may be stated numerically as a lambda value:

$$\lambda = \sqrt{\frac{\Sigma \, SD}{b}} \quad \begin{array}{l} (SD = \text{mean standard deviation} \\ b = \text{slope}) \end{array}$$

This is applicable to most bioassays. Calculation of precision for nonlinear assays or assays in which SD varies over the dose response area is more complex. Frequently a statement of SD is used for nonlinear assays in which the SD is calculated from duplicate determinations:

$$SD = \sqrt{\frac{D^2}{2\,N}} \quad \begin{array}{l} (D = \text{difference in duplicate determinations} \\ N = \text{number of duplicate determinations}) \end{array}$$

See references at the end of this chapter.

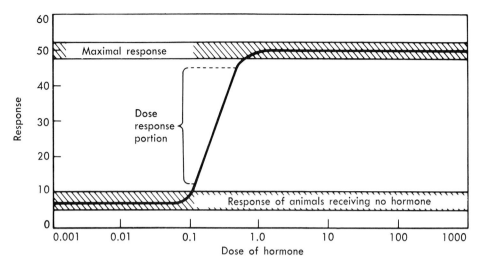

Fig. 1-1. Generalized dose response relations for a hormone assay system. On the ordinate is plotted the response in arbitrary units; on the abscissa, in arbitrary units, the dose of hormone. Only in the range between 0.12 and 0.9 "unit" of hormone do the increasing doses of hormone elicit increasing response. This is the dose response area.

sensitivity of the assay, where increasing doses of hormone produce no response (from 0.001 to 0.1 arbitrary unit in Fig. 1-1). This is followed by the *dose response portion,* an area where response is proportionate to dose. This is the useful portion of the assay. It is followed by an area of maximal response, where increasing doses of hormone produce no greater response; the response is maximal and cannot be stimulated further. Although we have defined the dose response portion as a limited part of the assay, the dose response curve includes the entire sigmoid curve with both maximal and minimal plateaus. As the generalities of various specific assay systems are reviewed, the reader should picture each assay in terms of this general dose response curve.*

---

*The dose response curve illustrated shows an increasing response with increasing doses of hormone administered. In some assays—for example, amount of ascorbic acid remaining in the ovary after luteinizing hormone injection—a decreasing response may be seen. The generalities discussed still apply and the curve drawn will merely be reversed, top to bottom.

POLYPEPTIDE HORMONES

There are four gonadotropic hormones of major interest to reproductive physiologists. All are carbohydrate-containing polypeptide hormones with similar biochemical and immunological properties. Each is composed of two polypeptide chains and, with the possible exception of human chorionic gonadotropin, each has a molecular weight of about 28,000.

1. Follicle-stimulating hormone (FSH). FSH is secreted by the pituitary gland of men and women. In women it acts to stimulate follicle growth in the ovary and, together with LH, to cause ovulation. In men it acts with LH to stimulate testicular tubule development and sperm formation.

2. Luteinizing hormone (LH). LH, sometimes called interstitial cell–stimulating hormone (ICSH), is also a pituitary hormone. It acts with FSH to cause ovulation in women and to stimulate interstitial cell development and testosterone production in men.

3. Prolactin or luteotropic hormone (LTH). Prolactin is a pituitary gonado-

tropin in rats and mice but is not known to function as such in humans. Its actions are very poorly understood in all mammals.

4. Chorionic gonadotropin. Nonpituitary sources of gonadotropins are rare. In higher primates and in humans, trophoblastic cells of the placenta secrete a gonadotropin called chorionic gonadotropin or human chorionic gonadotropin (HCG). Nonprimate mammals are not known to secrete chorionic gonadotropins. In pregnant mares (horse, donkey, or zebra) endometrial cups secrete a gonadotropin.

Other polypeptides may be indirectly involved in reproduction but are not included here. For example, overproduction or underproduction of thyrotropin and adrenocorticotropin may impair fertility.

Reference preparations

The gonadotropins have been quantified by two methods: bioassay and radioimmunoassay. Although their chemical structure is presently being elucidated, quantification of polypeptides by chemical methods is not yet practicable. Both bioassay and radioimmunoassay of gonadotropins have required use of a reference gonadotropin, a kind of "yardstick" for measurement. Ideally hormone potency would be stated in weights of 100% purified LH, FSH, or HCG (for example, 1 ml of blood contains 1×10^{-9} gram of LH). However, this is not yet feasible because gonadotropin preparations that are 100% pure have not been developed and the highly purified preparations are usually unstable, losing potency in storage. Thus impure gonadotropin preparations, which are easily available and which are stable over several years, are used. In early studies, investigators often stated potencies in terms of a bioassay response. For example, the amount of gonadotropin required to double the weight of the uterus in immature mice was a "mouse uterine weight unit." The variability of such a unit from animal strain to animal strain, from laboratory to laboratory, and even from time to time in a given laboratory made comparison of results unreliable. It was a major technical advance to have a large supply of a stable reference gonadotropin available for standardization of results. Such a standard is either used directly in every assay or is assayed against a more easily available local reference preparation, which in turn, is then used in every assay. In any case, results must always be stated in terms of the reference preparation. The second international reference preparation* of LH and FSH for human materials was prepared by extracting large volumes of urine from postmenopausal women. It is impure, contains both LH and FSH, and serves as a reference for both hormones. A separate reference preparation for HCG is also available and is impure.

Recent evidence has shown that when a reference preparation from an animal source is used for quantifying human pituitary hormones the relative potency of the two may differ with different bioassays. Furthermore, pituitary hormones from nonhuman sources generally fail to react at all in radioimmunoassays for human hormones—for example, bovine LH in the radioimmunoassay for human LH. For these reasons, it is necessary to use human reference preparations to quantify human gonadotropins. The story is even more complex, however, for it has been shown that pituitary LH may differ from urinary LH. Such data are exemplified in Table 1-2 and diagrammed in Fig. 1-2. Note in Table 1-2 that when "unknown" pituitary preparations were quantified in terms of the IRP HMG, a urinary reference preparation, the radioimmunoassay consistently gave much higher potency estimates. However, when the pituitary preparations were

---

*Second international reference preparation of human menopausal gonadotropin (IRP HMG No. 2).

Table 1-2. Bioassay and radioimmunoassay potency estimates for pituitary human LH preparations*†

Pituitary preparation	Potency by prostate weight bioassay		Potency by O A AD‡ bioassay		Potency by radioimmunoassay	
	IU/mg	Relative	IU/mg	Relative	IU/mg	Relative
A	62.8	1.0	126.1	1.0	232.3	1.0
B	3959	62.8	2614	20.7	11453	49.1
C	1692	27.0	1476	11.7	2834	12.1
D	691	10.9	569	4.5	2466	10.6
E	27.6	0.45	61.5	0.49	263	1.02

*Based on data from Odell, W. D., Reichert, L. E., and Bates, R. W.: In Margoulies, M., editor: Protein and polypeptide hormones, part I, 1968, Excerpta Medica Foundation, p. 124.
†Columns 1, 3, and 5 are potency estimates of pituitary preparations A to E, stated in terms of a urinary reference preparation (IRP HMG No. 2). Note that for all preparations the radioimmunoassay gave considerably higher estimates. Columns 2, 4, and 6 are potency estimates given in terms of an arbitrary pituitary reference preparation (A was assigned). Note that the radioimmunoassay estimates agree with either bioassay as well as one bioassay does with another.
‡Ovarian ascorbic acid depletion.

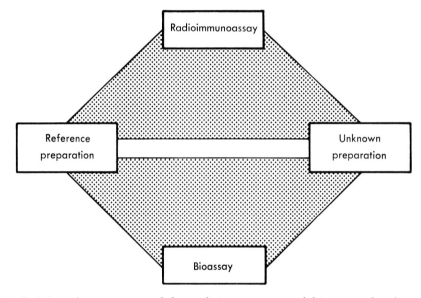

Fig. 1-2. Triangular systems used for radioimmunossay and bioassay of polypeptide hormones. Each assay system represents a different way of viewing the relationship between the reference preparation and the unknown preparation.

quantified in terms of a pituitary standard, radioimmunoassay potency estimates usually agreed with bioassay results as well as one bioassay agreed with another. In Fig. 1-2, consideration of each of the boxes is important in interpretation of exact potency values. Notice, however, that the *relative* potency of a preparation is similar in all assays. For example, in Table 1-2 prepara-

tion B is shown to be more potent than C, and C in turn more potent than A, no matter which assay system was used.

Although all this may be confusing to the reader, he may be reassured to know that it is also confusing to many so-called experts.

In summary, it may be said that any potency estimate must include a statement

Table 1-3. Approximate translation values for various gonadotropin preparations*

Material	International units (IU)	Assay
10 mouse uterine weight units†	1 IU HCG	Mouse uterine weight
1 IU HCG	0.8 IU (IRP HMG No. 2)‡	LH-HCG radioimmunoassay or specific LH bioassay
1 mg LER 907§	20 IU FSH (IRP HMG No. 2)	Rat ovarian weight augmentation bioassay
	38 IU FSH (IRP HMG No. 2)	FSH radioimmunoassay
	48 IU LH (IRP HMG No. 2)	Rat ventral prostate weight bioassay
	219 IU LH (IRP HMG No. 2)	LH radioimmunoassay
1 mg NIH-FSH-S1‖	26.5 IU FSH (IRP HMG No. 2)	Ovarian weight augmentation bioassay
1 mg NIH-LH-S1‖	51-67 IU (IRP HMG No. 2)	Rat ventral prostate weight bioassay
1 mg NIH-LH-S1‖	588-1538 IU (IRP HMG No. 2)	Ovarian ascorbic acid depletion bioassay

*See references 3 to 5. Caution must be used in interpreting radioimmunoassay conversion values. Those given here are means obtained by averaging results from several laboratories.
†Amount required to double uterine weight
‡Second international reference of human menopausal gonadotropin. This preparation is impure, contains LH and FSH, and serves as a reference for both.
§An impure pituitary gonadotropin distributed by the National Pituitary Agency and serving as an LH and FSH reference.
‖These materials from bovine pituitary do not react in radioimmunoassays for human LH, HCG, or FSH.

as to which assay was used and identification of the nature of the reference preparation. Table 1-3 presents some approximate conversion values for commonly used reference preparations.

Gonadotropin bioassays

Until 1960, all the polypeptide protein hormones were measured by using a biological response as an indicator. Biological fluids (plasma, serum, urine, etc.) or concentrates of these fluids were injected into animals and the response of some target tissue was measured. Such assays were often difficult to perform and highly dependent upon supplies of appropriate animals. As biological variability in response was decreased with the improvement in laboratory animals' breeding, such assays became more precise and in some instances more sensitive. Despite these improvements, variation in response from animal to animal remains a major limiting factor in precision of bioassays. (See Table 1-4.)

Bioassays will continue to be an important method of quantifying and identifying hormones. Even the more sensitive immunoassays need to be verified by correlating bioassay and immunoassay potency estimates whenever this is possible. At present, hormones are named and known in terms of the biological response they elicit. Thus it is a thyroid-stimulating hormone (TSH) that stimulates the thyroid gland to release thyroxine and triiodothyronine.* Any substance capable of producing this action would be called a thyroid-stimulating hormone.

Bioassays have limitations in sensitivity; unless approximately 100 ml is concentrated and extracted, specific bioassays are incapable of quantifying LH or FSH in serum or plasma from eugonadal men or women except at midcycle. Bioassay procedures have, therefore, generally been applied to pituitary extracts or to extracts or concentrates of 24 or more hours' urine

---

*TSH has a number of actions on the thyroid—including stimulating thyroxine release, increasing iodine uptake, and causing cellular hypertrophy and hyperplasia.

collection. Variations in urine collection, extraction, and concentration and in bioassay response may lead to imprecision of the answer. The general procedure for gonadotropin bioassay applied to urine includes, first, extracting and concentrating the gonadotropin and, second, injecting the extracts into assay animals at several different doses (e.g., undiluted extract, extract diluted 1:3, extract diluted 1:9, etc.). Recovery during extraction is variable, ranging from less than 25% to as much as 90% in series published by Martin[6,7] in 1964 and 1965 and averaging about 41% in urine from normal subjects. Table 1-5 gives results, using mouse uterine weight units, of bioassay of 110 consecutive 24-hour urine extracts obtained from two normal adult

Table 1-4. Gonadotropin assays

	Hormones eliciting reaction	Sensitivity (IRP HMG No. 2)* (IU)	Total amount injected per animal† (ml)	Time required for assay
Bioassay response‡				
Rat ovarian cholesterol depletion	LH, HCG	0.00005§	0.5	Hours?
Mouse uterine weight	LH, HCG, FSH	0.08	1.5-2.5	3-4 days
Rat uterine weight	LH, HCG, FSH	0.2	4	4-5 days
Rat ventral prostate weight	LH, HCG	0.2	2	4-5 days
Rat ovarian ascorbic acid depletion	LH, HCG	0.4	2	Hours
Rat ovarian hyperemia	LH, HCG	0.4	0.2	Hours
Rat testes weight	LH, HCG, FSH‖	1.0	4	4-5 days
Mouse uterine weight augmentation	FSH?	0.25	2.0	3-5 days
Rat ovarian weight augmentation	FSH	1.0	4	4-5 days
Radioimmunoassay				
LH	LH	0.001		3-5 days
FSH	FSH	0.001		3-5 days

*International units of the second international reference preparation of human menopausal gonadotropin. This preparation is impure, contains both LH, and FSH, and serves as a reference preparation for both.
†Total volume over entire assay period. Thus the rat prostate bioassay requires 5 days to perform and 0.5 ml is injected twice daily for 4 days. Animals are sacrificed on the fifth day.
‡All assays except the ovarian ascorbic acid depletion and the cholesterol depletion are performed in sexually immature animals and, often, hypophysectomized immature animals.
§This assay is very sensitive; however, there is a peculiar biphasic dose response curve that has limited its application. It is not generally used to quantify LH or HCG.
‖Predominantly an FSH response.

Table 1-5. Gonadotropin levels in 110 consecutive 24-hour urines from two menstruating women*

Patient	Number of days	Mouse uterine weight units				
		<10	10-50	50-200	200-500	>500
J. M.	56	11%	63%	20%	4%	2%
C. F.	54	18%	48%	24%	8%	2%
Average		15%		77%	8%	

*From Hertz, R., Odell, W. D., and Ross, G. T.: Diagnostic implications of primary amenorrhea, Ann. Intern. Med. 65:800, 1966.

women. The mouse uterine weight assay is the most sensitive and useful bioassay; but it is not specific, responding to LH, FSH, and HCG (the latter, of course, not normally present in urine from men or nonpregnant women). Note that 15% of the urines contained gonadotropins in amounts too little to be detected and that 8% of the urines contained greater than 200 mouse units, an amount usually found in urine from postmenopausal women or castrate men and women. Table 1-4 lists the majority of useful gonadotropin bioassays together with their relative sensitivity and specificities.

The prostate weight bioassay will be presented in some detail as an example. This assay was first described by Greep et al.[8] in 1941. Generally, hypophysectomized immature male rats are used; under the conditions described, increase in ventral prostate weight is caused only by injections of LH, HCG, or androgenic steroids (e.g., testosterone). Since the latter may be easily separated during extraction, this assay becomes specific for LH or HCG when injections of water-soluble materials are made. The general procedure in our laboratory is as follows:

Day 0 Hypophysectomized, 40- to 50-gram immature male rats are received from commercial source.
Day 1 The animals are divided into groups containing four or more animals each, and injections of gonadotropin solutions (0.5 ml twice daily subcutaneously) are begun.
Days 2 to 4 Twice daily injections are continued.
Day 5 Animals are sacrificed and the ventral lobe of the prostate is removed and weighed.

The reference preparation and unknowns are diluted and administered so that two or three groups of animals receive different

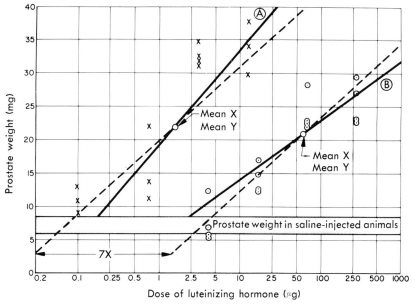

Fig. 1-3. An example of the prostate weight bioassay. A indicates one hormonal preparation and B another. It requires more of B to elicit the same prostate weight response as that obtained with a given dose of A. Each x represents the prostate weight of a single animal. Each solid line is a calculated regression line drawn through the mean dose (mean X) and the mean response (mean Y). Dashed lines indicate the regression lines using mean slopes from both preparations.

doses of each. Fig. 1-3 illustrates a typical prostate weight bioassay. In this example preparation B was the reference preparation and A was the unknown. Notice the scatter of the individual animals' responses. For calculating the potency of B in terms of A, only doses within the dose response area (Fig. 1-1) are used. The lowest dose of preparation B (4 μg) failed to produce a prostate weight significantly different from that of saline-injected control animals. Rats in this group could thus not be used. The mean dose (X) and mean response (Y) were calculated from the three other groups receiving preparation B and from all four groups with preparation A. The regression line (solid) was then calculated and drawn through mean X, mean Y. The slopes of these two regression lines were shown not to be significantly different; therefore, they were combined and parallel regression lines with the average slope drawn through each mean X, mean Y. It then could be determined that it required seven times as much B to produce the same prostate weight as was produced by any given amount of A.

The potency would be stated as A = 7.0 × B—by prostate weight bioassay using a reference preparation of urinary origin. Preparation B was the IRP HMG No. 2, which contains 8 IU/mg. We may thus state 1 mg of A = 56 (7 × 8) IU of LH by prostate weight bioassay.

One must also calculate the confidence limits (usually 95%) of the data and present these too. These calculations are tedious to perform by hand and, of course, a number of unknowns are usually quantified in one assay. Computer programs are available for rapid assessment of data. See references 9 to 11 for further details.

Gonadotropin immunoassay

Limitations in sensitivity and the complexity of bioassays have hastened acceptance of the simpler and more sensitive radioimmunoassay techniques for quantification of gonadotropins. The principles of a radioimmunoassay system may be illustrated by the equilibrium reaction shown in Fig. 1-4. Fig. 1-5 depicts dose response curves for purified LH from pituitary sources, for an impure preparation of urinary origin, and for crude pituitary powder. LH in serum also gives a dose response curve similar to each of these materials. The LH radioimmunoassay is about a hundred times more sensitive than the mouse uterine weight bioassay and may quantify LH in less than 1 ml of unextracted serum or plasma. Immunoassays are, however, not without problems. Quantification of hormones is based upon their immunological properties; biologically distinct hormones may have similar immunological properties. Thus human LH, FSH, and TSH appear to be more nearly immunologically similar than do bovine LH and human LH; yet obviously the last two are biologically related more closely. For further discussion see references 1 to 3, 11, and 12. Similar radioimmunoassays have been developed for FSH. Human FSH, LH, and TSH share many immunological properties. Each and every antiserum prepared for immunoassay of one must be tested to ensure little or no cross-reaction with the other two hormones. It is often a difficult task to obtain specific antisera.

Although radioimmunoassays are a great deal more sensitive than bioassays and *within a single assay* relative potencies are accurately determined, *absolute potencies* appear to be determined with about the same precision as by bioassay. Between-assay variability is significant, and accurate assessment of radioimmunoassay variability requires use of a variety of controls. Rodbard et al.[13] have recently reviewed this subject.

STEROID HORMONES

We shall consider three steroid hormones that are of major significance to reproduction.

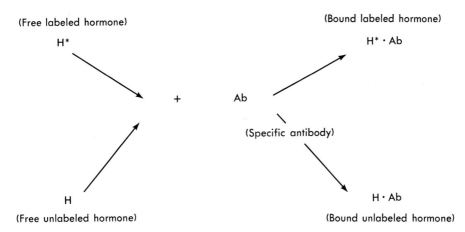

Fig. 1-4. Simplified scheme of the radioimmunossay, demonstrating competition of labeled hormone (*H**) and unlabeled hormone (*H*) in serum, urine, or a reference preparation, for a specific antibody (*Ab*). (From Swerdloff, R. S., and Odell, W. D.: Calif. Med. **109**:467, 1968.)

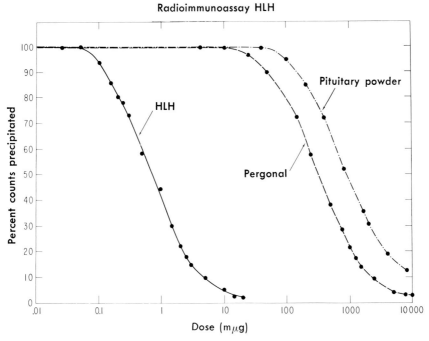

Fig. 1-5. Radioimmunoassay of human LH. HLH indicates a purified human LH preparation containing 8000 units/mg. Pergonal indicates an impure human urinary preparation containing LH and FSH. Pituitary powder is a saline extract of human pituitary powder. In this assay system, the antibody-bound radioactive LH is precipitated to separate it from radioactive LH that is not antibody-bound; these data are plotted on the Y axis. When plotted in this fashion, the dose response curve falls with increasing doses of LH. If nonantibody-bound radioactivity were plotted, the curve would resemble Fig. 1. (From Odell, W. D., Ross, G. T., and Rayford, P. L.: J. Clin. Invest. **46**:248, 1967.)

1. Estrogenic steroids. Estradiol is the major active estrogen secreted by the human ovary. It acts to stimulate uterine endometrial proliferation and the female secondary sex characteristics (breast development, body fat distribution, etc.) and feeds back in a complex way to control pituitary LH and FSH secretion.

2. Progestogens. Progesterone is the major progestogen secreted by the human ovary. It acts in concert with estradiol to transform the estrogen-stimulated uterine endometrium into a "secretory" endometrium and to control pituitary LH and FSH secretion.

3. Androgens. Testosterone is the major androgen secreted by the testis. It acts to stimulate male secondary sex characteristics and the sex accessory structures (penis, prostate, etc.) and, in feedback, to control pituitary LH secretion. These steroid hormones have been quantified by bioassay, chemical assay, and competitive binding assay.

Bioassay

Bioassays for the steroid hormones mentioned have been developed, using the secondary sex characteristics or sex accessory organs in immature animals as responsive tissues. These tissues also respond to endogenous gonadal steroids in response to administration of gonadotropins. However, the marked differences in chemical properties of steroids and gonadotropins make separation relatively easy prior to administration. In addition, castrated animals fail to respond to gonadotropins but do respond to gonadal steroids. Fig. 1-6 depicts a dose response curve for estradiol in the uterine weight bioassay. In brief, this bioassay[14] was performed as follows:

1. Immature female rats weighing 34 to 39 grams were divided into groups.

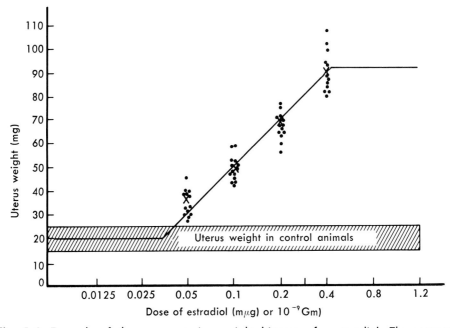

Fig. 1-6. Example of the mouse uterine weight bioassay for estradiol. The response to the standard or known amounts of hormone is presented. (Modified from Lauson, H. D., Heller, C. G., Golden, J. B., and Sevringhaus, E. L.: Endocrinology **24**:35, 1939.)

2. Estradiol-containing solutions, 0.5 ml, were administered subcutaneously twice daily for 3 days (days 1 to 3).
3. On the fourth day, each animal was sacrificed and the uterus removed, drained of fluid, blotted, and weighed.

Bioassays other than those listed exist for all three kinds of steroid hormones under discussion (estrogens, androgens, and progestogens). An insensitive but specific test for progestogens is based on transformation of the estrogen-stimulated rabbit uterus endometrium into the secretory form (Clauberg test).

Double isotope derivative assays

The development of double isotope derivative methods for steroid hormone measurement represented a major advance in endocrinology because of the marked increase in sensitivity over bioassays. The methods are tedious and time-consuming; frequently only five to ten samples may be quantified each week. The principle of these methods is as follows: A known amount of the steroid in radioactive form (e.g., ^{14}C steroid) is added to an unknown sample to assess loss of hormone during purification procedures. The sample is then subjected to a variety of extraction and chromatographic procedures to isolate and purify the steroid to be measured. After purification all the steroid isolate (^{14}C, labeled and unlabeled) is labeled with a second radioisotope (e.g., ^3H). This mixture is then further purified until $^3H/^{14}C$ is constant. The amount of steroid is quantified by a sensitive technique such as gas chromatography. Losses during extraction are calculated through the final recovery of ^{14}C. Details of the determination of testosterone by this method are presented as an example.

Double isotope derivative method of quantifying plasma testosterone.[16] The method described here is a technically difficult and time-consuming procedure. Testosterone-^{14}C is added to a 10 to 20 ml plasma sample (to assess losses of testosterone during extraction), and the sample is extracted with an ether-chloroform mixture. The extract is dried and applied to a thin-layer chromatogram, which is developed in benzene–ethyl acetate. Epitestosterone and testosterone are eluted together and the eluate is dried and rechromatographed in benzene–ethyl acetate to separate the two steroids. The testosterone eluate is acetylated with ^3H–acetic anhydride, and unlabeled (carrier) testosterone is added. The extracts are then washed, dried, and run on two more chromatograms to purify the ^3H–testosterone acetate. The testosterone acetate is then converted to o-methyloxime, and the testosterone-o-methyloximes chromatographed again. Final purification is accomplished by dissolving these eluates in ethanol and injecting them into a gas-liquid chromatograph. The portion of this column effluent corresponding to the o-methyloximes is collected on p-terphenyl, which in turn is placed in a counting vial; the ^3H and ^{14}C are counted separately.

The plasma testosterone level in $\mu g/100$ ml then is equal to

$$\frac{^3H}{^{14}C} \times \frac{^{14}Ca}{S.A.} - t \frac{100}{V}$$

where

$^3H/^{14}C$ = tritium to carbon ratio of the final sample
^{14}Ca = cpm of ^{14}C steroid marker added to plasma
S.A. = specific activity of the $^3H^+$ – acetic anhydride in cpm/μg testosterone
t = mass of ^{14}C steroid marker added
V = volume of plasma extracted

Values in normal men have averaged 0.46 $\mu g/100$ ml and in normal women, 0.04 $\mu g/100$ ml. (See Table 1-6.)

Competitive binding assays

The principles of steroid competitive binding assays are identical to those described under radioimmunoassays. Antibodies against steroid-albumin conjugates

Table 1-6. Some androgen and estrogen assays

Assay	Substance measured	Approximate sensitivity
Mouse uterine weight	Estrogens + androgens*	50,000 micromicrograms† of estradiol
Rat seminal vesicle weight	Androgens	100,000 $\mu\mu$g of testosterone
Rat ventral prostate weight	Androgens	100,000 $\mu\mu$g of testosterone
Comb growth in chicks	Androgens	200,000 $\mu\mu$g of testosterone
Double isotope derivative	Estradiol‡	800 $\mu\mu$g§
Double isotope derivative	Testosterone	1,000 $\mu\mu$g
Competitive binding assay‖	Estradiol	10 $\mu\mu$g
Competitive binding assay	Testosterone	10 $\mu\mu$g

*The main stimuli are estrogens, but testosterone also increases uterine weight.
†10^{-12} grams ($\mu\mu$g).
‡Chemical methods require extensive purification of the sample prior to its measurement. Any single steroid may be specifically determined by isolating it alone.
§Theoretically, sensitivity is limited only by specific activity of isotopes.
‖Two binding hormones have been used to measure estrogens: (1) the uterine estrogen receptor protein and (2) antibodies against estradiol-albumin conjugates.

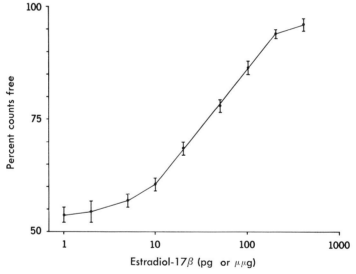

Fig. 1-7. Dose response curve for estradiol in the radioimmunoassay. The binding protein used in this assay was an antiserum directed against estradiol conjugated to albumin. Korenman and associates[18] have developed a highly specific estrogen assay using rabbit uterine receptor as the binding protein. (From Abraham, G. E.: J. Clin. Endocr. **29**:866, 1969.)

have been prepared and used for assay purposes.[17] The uterine-protein-estrogen binder, a highly specific binding protein with high affinity, has been used by Korenman et al.[18] for assay of estradiol. Androgen-binding serum proteins have been used to quantify androgens.[19] Cortisol-binding globulin (CBG) has been used to quantify cortisol, progesterone, and 17-hydroxy-progesterone.[20] Serum proteins such as CBG may bind a variety of steroids. Specificity is achieved, as it is in double isotope derivative methods, by purification of the sample prior to quantification. Many of these methods are difficult to perform, but continued simplification and improved technology will undoubtedly lead to their widespread use. Fig. 1-7 illustrates a dose response curve for estradiol in the radio-immunoassay developed by Abraham.[17]

CONCLUSIONS

Chapter 1 has introduced the reader to the variety of methods used to quantify gonadotropins and gonadal steroids. All the data presented in the pages to follow were obtained by utilizing these methods. Furthermore, reading published literature on reproductive physiology requires some familiarity with these methods and their various advantages and limitations.

REFERENCES

1. Odell, W. D., Reichert, L. E., and Bates, R. W.: Pitfalls in the radioimmunoassay of carbohydrate containing polypeptides. In Margoulies, M., editor: Protein and polypeptide hormones, part I, New York, 1968, Excerpta Medica Foundation.
2. Odell, W. D., Reichert, L. E., and Swerdloff, R. S.: Correlation between bioassay and immunoassay of human luteinizing hormone. In Rosemberg, E., editor: Gonadotropins—1968, proceedings of the workshop conference at Vista Hermosa, Mexico, June 24-26, 1968, Los Altos, Calif., 1968, Geron-X, Inc.
3. Albert, A., Rosemberg, E., Ross, G. T., Paulsen, C. A., and Ryan, R. J.: Report of the National Pituitary Agency collaborative study on the radioimmunoassay of FSH and LH, J. Clin. Endocr. 28:1214, 1968.
4. Swerdloff, R. S., and Odell, W. D.: Gonadotropins: present concepts in the human, Calif. Med. 109:467, 1968.
5. Reichert, L. E.: Further studies on the purification of human postmenopausal urinary luteinizing hormone, Endocrinology 80:319, 1967.
6. Martin, F. I. R.: Variation in the recovery of gonadotropins from hypopituitary urine, Aust. Ann. Med. 13:77, 1964.
7. Martin, F. I. R.: Pituitary gonadotropins in urine. The recovery of added gonadotropins from normal urine, Aust. J. Exp. Biol. Med. Sci. 43:315, 1965.
8. Greep, R. O., VanDyke, H. B., and Chow, B. F.: Use of the anterior lobe of the prostate gland in assay of metakentrin, Proc. Soc. Exp. Biol. Med. 46:644, 1941.
9. Finney, D. H.: Statistical methods in biological assay, London, 1952, Charles Griffin Co., Ltd.
10. Cooper, J. A.: A new computer program for the statistical evaluation of biologic assay data (a manual for users), Bethesda, Md., undated, Endocrinology and Metabolism Branch, National Institute of Child Health and Human Development, National Institutes of Health.
11. Odell, W. D., Ross, G. T., and Rayford, P. L.: Radioimmunoassay for luteinizing hormone in human plasma or serum: physiological studies, J. Clin. Invest. 46:248, 1967.
12. Odell, W. D., Parlow, A. F., Cargille, C. M., and Ross, G. T.: Radioimmunoassay for human follicle-stimulating hormone: Physiological studies, J. Clin. Invest. 47:2551, 1968.
13. Rodbard, D., Rayford, P. L., Cooper, J. A., and Ross, G. T.: Statistical quality control of radioimmunoassays, J. Clin. Endocr. 28:1412, 1968.
14. Lauson, H. D., Heller, C. G., Golden, J. B., and Sevringhaus, E. L.: The immature rat uterus in the assay of estrogenic substances, and a comparison of estradiol, estrone, and estriol, Endocrinology 24:35, 1939.
15. Baird, D. T.: A method for measurement of estrone and estradiol-17-beta in peripheral human blood and other biological fluids using 35S pipsyl chloride, J. Clin. Endocr. 28:244, 1968.
16. Bardin, C. W., and Lipsett, M. B.: Estimation of testosterone and androstenedione in human peripheral plasma, Steroids 9:71, 1967.
17. Abraham, G. E.: Solid-phase radioimmunoassay of estradiol-17β, J. Clin. Endocr. 29:866, 1969.
18. Korenman, S. G., Perrin, L. E., and McCallum, T. P.: A radio-ligand binding assay system for estradiol measurement in human plasma, J. Clin. Endocr. 29:879, 1969.
19. Horton, R., Kato, T., and Sherins, R.: A rapid method for the estimation of testosterone in male plasma, Steroids 10:245, 1967.
20. Murphy, B. E. P.: Some studies of the protein-binding of steroids and their application to the routine micro and ultra-micro measurement of various steroids in body fluids by competitive protein binding radioassay, J. Clin. Endocr. 27:973, 1967.

CHAPTER 2

The central nervous system–hypothalamus–pituitary unit

The hypothalamus represents a prominent portion of the brain in all vertebrates. Its general location and connections are represented in Fig. 2-1. By definition, the hypothalamus lies below the thalamus and, in effect, comprises the lateral walls of the lower part of the third ventricle. According to Daniel,[1] the rostral boundary is marked as a plane lying just rostral to the optic chiasm. Its caudal boundary may be defined as a coronal plane just posterior to the mammillary bodies. The lateral boundaries are the most difficult to define, but at various levels the following structures may be found situated laterally: the lowermost part of the thalamus, the internal capsule, the globus pallidus, the ansa lenticularis, and the optic tract. Inferiorly, in the hypothalamus of man, the walls of the third ventricle form a funnel-shaped cavity, the infundibulum (or tuber cinereum), which extends downward to form the pituitary stalk. This prominent area at the origin of the stalk has also been called the median eminence area.

As may be seen in Figs. 2-1 to 2-4, the pituitary stalk ends at the pituitary gland. The pituitary is a rounded body formed of two embryologically distinct portions: the anterior lobe, an upgrowth from the primitive mouth cavity, and a posterior lobe derived from a neural downgrowth from the floor of the diencephalon. The posterior lobe is thus directly connected to the hypothalamus; nerve axons course down the stalk and into the lobe from the supraoptic and paraventricular nuclei. This complex (supraoptic-paraventricular areas and posterior pituitary) controls and secretes antidiuretic hormone and oxytocin. The anterior lobe is not directly connected to the hypothalamus; central nervous system control of anterior lobe secretion is exerted via an unusual blood vascular supply. All the blood supplying this lobe is derived from vessels that begin in a capillary bed in the median eminence. These capillaries progressively coalesce to form the long portal vessels, which course down the pituitary stalk into the anterior lobe and again break into capillaries. From the anterior lobe sinusoids, blood is drained into short veins that enter the venous sinuses around the pars distalis. Hypothalamic control over anterior pituitary function is exerted by specific releasing factors or inhibiting factors that are elaborated in the hypothalamus and pass via these portal vessels to the anterior lobe where they result in specific stimulation or inhibition of secretion of a number of polypeptide hormones. The blood supply of the posterior lobe is of the usual sort; two arteries spring from the internal carotid arteries within the cavernous sinuses. These inferior hypophyseal arteries run medially to form an arterial ring that encircles the posterior lobe; small branches from this ring ramify within the neural tissue of the posterior lobe. The blood supply to the hypothalamus is derived from small

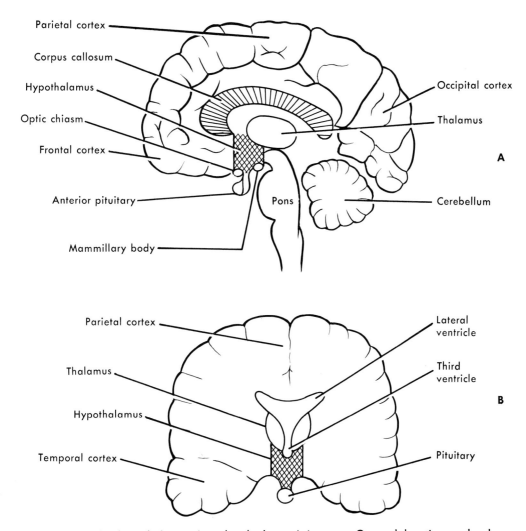

Fig. 2-1. The hypothalamus (crosshatched area) in man. General location and relations are shown in sagittal section (**A**) and in coronal section (**B**).

arteries arising from the circle of Willis. This vascular area roughly outlines the hypothalamus at the base of the brain.

The hypothalamus contains a large number of nuclei, some well-defined, some difficult to define. Definite endocrine or physiological roles cannot presently be assigned to all these nuclei. As seen in Fig. 2-2, two of the most prominent hypothalamic nuclei are the supraoptic and paraventricular nuclei. The supraoptic nucleus straddles the rostral portion of the optic tract just caudal

to the optic chiasm. The cells in this nucleus are large and its blood supply is particularly rich. Two other prominent nuclei, the mammillary, form the rounded swellings located at the caudal borders of the hypothalamus. These nuclei are called mammillary bodies and are larger in man than in other species. For details concerning some of the other nuclei, consult references listed at the end of this chapter.

Interconnections of these various nuclei with each other and with other portions

15

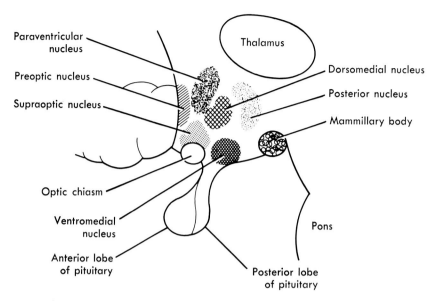

Fig. 2-2. Diagrammatic presentation of hypothalamic nuclei in man.

of the central nervous system are incompletely understood. Some of the known relationships are diagrammed in Fig. 2-3. One prominent *input* tract is the fornix, a massive column of myelinated nerve fibers that originate in the hippocampus and dentate gyrus on the medial aspect of the temporal lobe. The column sweeps upward to the lower surface of the corpus callosum, continues forward to separate, forming the anterior columns of the fornix, then dives down to end in the mammillary nuclei. The second input tract arises in the frontal lobe and cornu ammonis (on the temporal lobe) and passes to various hypothalamic nuclei. The relationships appear to be specific; a given locus of the cortex sends messages to a given hypothalamic nucleus. These connections originate over much of the prefrontal and premotor areas.

Outflow tracts are shown diagrammatically in Fig. 2-4. The prominent mammillary nuclei send fibers to the thalamus (anterior nucleus), which in turn sends fibers to the cornu ammonis. Thus a closed circuit is possible, for the cornu ammonis sends fibers back to various hypothalamic nuclei. A

second closed circuit also potentially exists, in which mammillary and other hypothalamic projections reach the thalamus, which in turn sends projections to the frontal cortex; the frontal cortex returns fibers to the hypothalamus. These closed circuits may be in part the physical basis for emotions. The greater portion of the frontal lobe cortex must be regarded as a projection area from the hypothalamus via the thalamus.[5] The mammillothalamic tract (bundle of Vicq d'Azyr) is also an outflow tract. It sends a bundle of fibers, the mammillotegmental tract, to the tegmental region of the midbrain. This tract joins the dorsal longitudinal fasciculus and eventually distributes fibers to the reticular formation in the brainstem. The ventromedial and dorsomedial nuclei of the hypothalamus have extensive interconnections to other hypothalamic nuclei and probably to the subthalamic area and various thalamic nuclei as well. Another major outflow tract is the supraoptic–paraventricular–posterior pituitary system previously mentioned.

The hypothalamic nuclei are presently believed to control the secretion of neurohor-

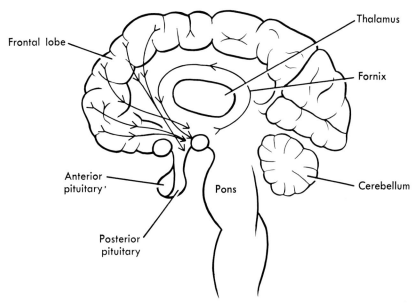

Fig. 2-3. Afferent pathways to the hypothalamus. There are some physiological data suggesting a brainstem hypothalamic tract, but this is not described anatomically and is not shown on this diagram.

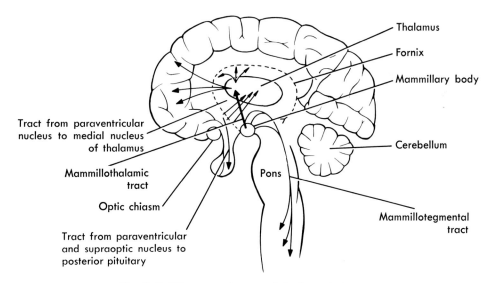

Fig. 2-4. Efferent pathways of the hypothalamus.

monal substances released into the pituitary portal circulation for the regulation of specific anterior pituitary hormone secretion. There are some suggestions (but not unanimity of opinion) that specific hypothalamic areas have portal flow to specific pituitary areas. Receptor sites for hormonal feedback information seem to lie within the hypothalamus or at the pituitary level, or both, depending on the particular hormones.

(Details of gonadotropin control will be discussed in later chapters.) For example, thyrotropin-releasing factor (TRF), from the hypothalamus, stimulates pituitary TSH secretion; but thyroxine inhibition of TSH secretion occurs at a pituitary level and results in inhibition of the effects of TRF. The details of such hypothalamic control mechanisms are currently subjects of major investigation and of great controversy. Abundant evidence exists to demonstrate that pituitary secretion of LH and FSH is controlled predominantly via the central nervous system (hypothalamus). A luteinizing hormone–releasing factor (LRF)[7,8] and a follicle-stimulating hormone–releasing factor (FRF)[9] have been identified and isolated from hypothalamic tissue.* Similar releasing factors have been isolated from hypothalamic tissue and identified for TSH, growth hormone, and adrenocorticotropin. Factors that *inhibit* pituitary secretion of melanocyte-stimulating hormone and prolactin have been identified. Early studies by Guillemin et al.[7] and by Ramirez and McCann[8] suggested that the gonadotropin-releasing factors were small polypeptides (molecular weight, 1000 to 5000). It has recently been shown that TRF is a tripeptide (pyrol-glutamic-histidyl-proline amide). The amino acid composition of LRF and FRF is unknown, but they appear to be larger than TRF.[11,12]

The epithelial cells of the anterior pituitary do not differ strikingly from one another in size and shape. However, using special staining techniques, it is possible to differentiate several cell types. A variety of human pituitary disease states, some associated with pituitary tumors and overproduction of single pituitary hormones, have been studied to correlate cytology and hormone production. In acromegaly, for example, growth hormone secretion was attributed to acidophilic cells. Typically these are large cells with coarse granules which take up acidic stains and thus stain red with the usual hematoxylin and eosin stain. In Cushing's disease, adrenocorticotropin was attributed to the basophilic cells. Typically these cells contain granules staining with basic dyes and appearing purple with hematoxylin. Chromophobe cells do not stain well with hematoxylin and eosin, and for years no endocrine function was attributed to them.

In 1963 Ezrin and Murray[14] published a valuable addition to the endocrine literature, summarizing Ezrin's work of many years. Using a variety of staining techniques (aldehyde-thionine combined with periodic acid–Schiff), they were able to identify seven types of pituitary cells. By correlating pituitary histology with endocrine disease states both in humans and in animal studies where single pituitary hormones were hypersecreted or suppressed, these workers suggested a one-to-one relationship between cell type and pituitary hormone secretion. At present, most pituitary histologists agree that one cell type secretes FSH and another cell type secretes LH. Recall from Chapter 1 that TSH, LH, and FSH have similar biochemical and immunochemical structures.

The hypothalamic region is involved in a variety of important physiological control mechanisms other than pituitary hormone secretion. These include temperature regulation, appetite, thirst, some aspects of cardiovascular interrelations, and many aspects of emotional display. These subjects do not form a pertinent area for discussion in this text on reproductive physiology but the interested reader may refer to additional references.

---

*Each of these releasing factors has now been identified in human hypothalamic tissue.[10] TRF has been administered to humans and shown to be highly effective in releasing TSH.[13]

REFERENCES

1. Daniel, P. M.: The anatomy of the hypothalamus and pituitary gland. In Martini, L., and Ganong, W. F., editors: Neuroendocrinology, New York, 1967, Academic Press, Inc.

2. Harris, G. W.: Neural control of the pituitary gland, London, 1955, Edward Arnold & Co.

3. le Gros Clark, W. E.: The topography and homologies of the hypothalamic nuclei in man, J. Anat. 70:203, 1936.

4. Netter, F. H.: The Ciba collection of medical illustrations. I. Nervous system, Summit, R. J., 1953, Ciba Pharmaceutical Products, Inc.

5. le Gros Clark, W. E.: The connections of the frontal lobes of the brain, Lancet 1:353, 1948.

6. Everett, J. W.: Central neural control of reproductive function, Physiol. Rev. 44:373, 1964.

7. Guillemin, R., Jutisz, M., and Sakiz, E.: Purification partielle d'un facteur hypothalamique (LRF) stimulant la secretion de l'hormone hypophysaire de luteinisation (LH), C. R. Acad. Sci. 256:504, 1963.

8. Ramirez, V. D., and McCann, S. M.: Thioglycolate-stable luteinizing hormone and corticotropin-releasing factors, Amer. J. Physiol. 207:441, 1964.

9. Igarashi, M., and McCann, S. M.: A hypothalamic follicle stimulating hormone-releasing factor, Endocrinology 74:446, 1964.

10. Shally, A. U., Müller, E. E., Arimura, A., Bowers, C. Y., Saito, T., Redding, T. W., Sawano, S., and Pizzolato, P.: Releasing factors in human hypothalamic and neurohypophysial extracts, J. Clin. Endocr. 27:755, 1967.

11. Burgus, R., Dunn, T. F., Desiderio, D., Ward, D. N., Vale, W., and Guillemin, R.: Characterization of ovine hypothalamic hypophysiotropic TSH-releasing factor, Nature 226:321, 1970.

12. Nair, R. M. G., Barrett, J. F., Bowers, C. Y., and Shally, A. V.: Structure of porcine thyrotropin releasing hormone, Biochemistry 9:1103, 1970.

13. Fleischer, N., Burgus, R., Vale, W., Dunn, T. F., and Guillemin, R.: Preliminary observations on the effect of synthetic thyrotropin releasing factor on plasma thyrotropin levels in man, J. Clin. Endocr. 31:109, 1970.

14. Ezrin, C., and Murray, S.: The cells of the human adenohypophysis in pregnancy, thyroid disease, and adrenal cortical disorders. In Benoit, J., and DaLage, C., editors: Cytologie de l'adénohypophyse, Paris, 1963, Colloques Internationaux du Centre National de la Recherche Scientifique.

CHAPTER 3

The ovary and the female sex accessories

THE OVARY

In the female, the gonad serves several functions in the sequence of the reproductive process. These include (1) preparatory development of the reproductive tract through the production of hormones, (2) release of ova, and (3) development of a favorable environment for the transport, implantation, and nourishment of the blastocyst. To accomplish these processes, follicular development, ovulation, and corpus luteum formation occur cyclically and result in the production and secretion of estrogens and progestogens. Biosynthesis and secretion of these hormones are mediated in a heterogeneous cell population that in turn is initiated and regulated by the gonadotropins. The hormones secreted at each stage affect gonadotropin secretion by either stimulation or suppression. These interrelationships are discussed in greater detail in Chapter 5.

Anatomical structure

The ovaries undergo cyclical changes in histological structure throughout their lifetime. The ovary of the newborn is a delicate elongated structure that will gradually enlarge and change in shape and position between birth and pubescence. The adult ovary is almond shaped, measuring approximately 3.5 × 2 cm with a thickness of about 1.5 cm. The combined weight of the two ovaries is between 4 and 8 grams. The external surface is usually uneven as a result of scars of previous ovulation and atretic follicles. The upper (tubal) pole of the ovary is rounded and is attached to a suspensory ligament. The lower pole is more pointed and is attached to the uterus by a fibromuscular coat (the uteroovarian ligament). Recently ruptured follicles may be identified by single or multiple reddish elevation(s) measuring several millimeters in diameter. The corpus luteum is formed from the ruptured follicle and appears yellow, measuring from a few millimeters to several centimeters. It usually cannot be identified on the external surface until a cut section is made. The normal corpus luteum ranges from a solid structure of about 1 × 1.5 cm to a cystic or hemorrhagic structure measuring up to 4 cm or greater in diameter. These structures may occupy as much as one half to two thirds of the total ovarian volume and they contain a great deal of dark blood in the center surrounded by a thin rim of yellow tissue.

The source of the ovarian artery supply is an anastomosis of the ovarian and uterine vessels (Fig. 3-1). The main ovarian trunk contains branches that enter the hilum and are further subdivided into two tortuous and undulating medullary branches. They proceed to opposite poles of the ovary, giving off spiral cortical branches in a counterclockwise direction. The cortical branches again divide into arterioles which supply a group of follicles. The circulatory system of the ovary must make continuous adjustments to major variations in size and to the changing needs of

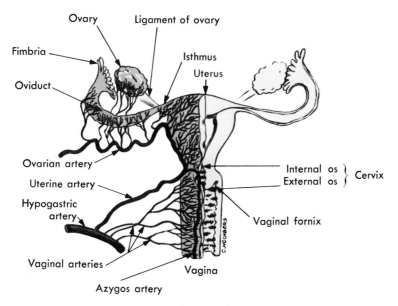

Fig. 3-1. Female reproductive system.

the active hormone-secreting cells.[1] The reduction of blood pressure from the ovarian arteries and the equalization of blood flow within the ovaries are determined by the tortuosity of the conducting system, the angle of branching, and the diameter of the branch to the main stem. In this manner, an abundant and uniform supply of blood is distributed under reduced pressure.

Growth and atresia of the ovum

Fetal development. During early embryogenesis, large ameboid primordial germ cells migrate from the yolk sac to a localized portion of peritoneum in the body of the embryo.[2] There are about a thousand germ cells during the fifth week of gestation, but this number is increased by mitosis to about one-half million at the time of birth. Rapid division of the primitive germ cells and the contiguous mesenchymal cells causes the formation of a prominent genital ridge which projects into the body cavity. The medial slope of the genital ridge develops into the primitive undifferentiated gonad. This gonad later divides into cortical and medullary portions in

both sexes. By the third gestational month, the ovarian section consists of cortex with a mass of germ cells and mesenchymal cells. The size of the germ cells (now called oogonia) is rapidly reduced as mitosis proceeds, comparable to the size of the surrounding mesenchymal cells. Mitotic activity of the germ cells is maximal between the eighth and twentieth weeks of gestation. In the medullary region, germ cells are distinguished by large irregular clumps of nuclear chromatin, which are quite different from the chromosomes of the oogonial divisions. This change marks the beginning of synapsis that involves interactions between pairs of chromosomes. During the fourth gestational month, some of these cells after undergoing synapsis begin to enlarge and are termed primary oocytes. Germ cell mitosis slows down after the twentieth week, ceasing at birth, and many of the oocytes that have developed begin to degenerate. A covering of mesenchymal cells (now called follicular or granulosa cells) encloses the primary oocytes, and this cellular unit is called a primordial follicle. Primordial follicles are first seen in the medulla and later in the

21

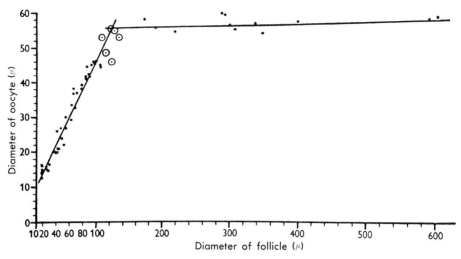

Fig. 3-2. Relation of the size of the oocyte to that of the follicle in the rat. (From Mandl, A. M., and Zuckerman, S.: J. Endocr. **8:**126, 1952.)

cortex. Some enlarge before birth and others remain unchanged prior to menopause.

Postnatal development and maturity. The number of follicles at the time of birth ranges from 150,000 to 500,000. By puberty, this number becomes reduced by an unknown process.[3] In the child, the ovary is composed of a cortex filled with large numbers of closely packed primordial follicles with those in the center of the cortex being in the most advanced stages of development. Although the cortex is relatively thin in young women, the primordial follicles are separated by bands of connective tissue. There is also a gradual decline of oocytes after puberty to a mean of 34,-000[4] and by menopause, few remain. It has been estimated that during the reproductive life of a woman only 300 to 400 oocytes undergo maturation and are extruded by the process of ovulation; the remainder undergo some form of atresia. In most mammals, the size of the oocyte in the primary follicle remains uniform until development into mature follicles. The primordial oocyte in the mature human ovary ranges in size from 10 to 180 μ. In the preovulatory follicle, the oocytes have increased in size and range from 120 to 150 μ. In the rat, the diameter of the primordial oocyte is similar to that in

the human, but in the preovulatory follicle, the oocyte is smaller (about 55 μ) (Fig. 3-2).

Follicular growth in the sexually mature woman

In the mature ovary, the primary follicle consists of a relatively large oogonium enclosed by a single layer of granulosa cells.[6] Under the influence of local stimulator(s) in the ovarian cortex, the follicle cells proliferate and become stratified while the oocyte increases in size. The follicle is known at this stage as a secondary follicle. When the primary oocyte has increased to twice its original diameter, a thick membrane (the zona pellucida) develops around it. The granulosa cells continue mitotic division and form a thicker layer of cells, probably influenced by FSH from the pituitary. Fluid begins to accumulate between the cells, cavitation occurs, and further development results in an antrum filled with follicular fluid. The follicle is now known as a secondary follicle or a graafian follicle.[7] The ovum, now a secondary oocyte, projects into the large pool of fluid and is surrounded by several layers of granulosa cells, known as a cumulus oophorus (Fig. 3-3).

The early primordial follicle (composed

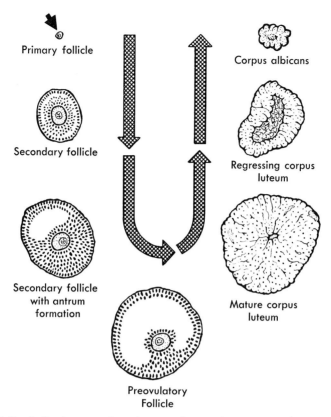

Primary follicle

Secondary follicle

Secondary follicle
with antrum
formation

Preovulatory
Follicle

Corpus albicans

Regressing corpus
luteum

Mature corpus
luteum

Fig. 3-3. Follicular growth and corpus luteum formation and regression.

of oogonia and granulosa cells) is devoid of additional cellular coverings. As the follicle develops, however, the ovarian stroma surrounding the follicle forms an investing layer of specialized cells (the theca). As the follicles enlarge under the influence of FSH, the theca of the fully developed follicle is differentiated into two layers. The innermost layer (theca interna) is composed of polyhedral cells and contains many capillaries; the outer layer (theca externa), which is less vascular, is made up of fusiform cells. Blood vessels do not enter the granulosa layer. These follicles often become so large that a bulge appears on the ovarian surface.

In the physiological menstrual cycle, follicles enlarge by accumulating great amounts of antral fluid in preparation for ovulation. Under normal circumstances,

only one of these ten to fifteen enlarged follicles undergoes ovulation in each cycle. Multiple ovulations take place in humans and monkeys in approximately 1% to 2% of all cycles. The process by which one follicle in each cycle is selected for ovulation with regression of others is not yet fully understood.

In each menstrual cycle, nonovulating follicles undergo a degenerative process known as atresia. In the next cycle, the development of another set of follicles is required for ovulation to take place. During the process of atresia, the zona pellucida becomes hyalinized and crenated, the ovum is invaded by round cells, and the chromatin material is lysed. There is subsequent absorption of the follicular fluid (liquor folliculi), and the follicular layers that show necrobiotic changes are replaced by fibrous tissue which later becomes hyalinized. The fibrous tissue scar is known as a corpus atreticum and may persist for long periods of time. On occasion, a cyst may develop if the liquor of a large follicle is not completely absorbed.

Oogenesis

The process of maturation of the primitive oogonium to the mature ovum is termed oogenesis. The germ cells initially undergo multiple mitotic divisions and later this is followed by meiosis or a division of the chromatin material (Fig. 3-4). Some germ cells remain dormant and may not mature for 40 years, whereas others reach maturity and are fertilized as early as 12 years after oogenesis commences.

Shortly after migration of primitive germ cells from the yolk sac to the medial slope of the mesonephric ridge, mitosis occurs. The rate of cellular division is maximal dur-

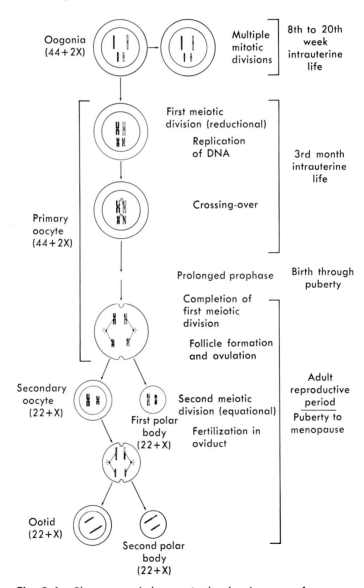

Fig. 3-4. Chromosomal changes in the development of an ovum.

ing the eighth to the twentieth week of gestation; then it gradually decreases and finally ceases before birth. By quantitative DNA measurements, it has been shown that early oocytes contain twice as much nuclear DNA as their somatic cells; this is essentially the same amount present in the equatorial plate of the first maturation division. By the end of the twelfth gestational week, some oogonia develop into larger cells (primary oocytes), at which time they enter a long prophase of the first meiotic division, resulting in reduction of the diploid number of chromosomes (44 autosomes and 2 sex chromosomes) to the haploid number (22 autosomes and 1 sex chromosome). At the time of birth, the oocytes are in the long prophase of their first meiotic division; they remain in that stage until the development of the follicles, which may begin as early as puberty.

The first meiotic division is completed in the mature follicle prior to ovulation. The primary oocyte then divides into two daughter cells of unequal size, each containing 23 chromosomes. The cell receiving the majority of cytoplasm is termed the secondary oocyte; the smaller cell, which is known as the first polar body, lies between the zona pellucida and the vitelline membrane of the secondary oocyte. The second maturation division takes place in the ampulla of the oviduct and occurs only if the ovum is fertilized (Chapter 9). Ovulation occurs as the spindle begins to form, preceding metaphase in the secondary oocyte. If the human ovum does not meet a viable spermatozoon within approximately 24 hours after ovulation, it begins to degenerate. Fertilized ova have occasionally been accompanied by three polar bodies, and it is thought that the first polar body undergoes subsequent division.

Ovulation and corpus luteum formation

Release of the ovum from a mature follicle takes place shortly after a high peak of LH and FSH. The sequence of events following the LH-FSH peak and causing ovulation is still uncertain, but these factors have been suggested: (1) alterations of vascular flow, producing necrobiosis at the dome of the protruding follicle, (2) increased intrafollicular pressure resulting from depolymerization of acid mucopolysaccharides, and (3) local proteolytic action on the dome of the follicle.[8] Under direct vision, the rupture and discharge of the contents of the human follicle have been noted to appear slowly rather than explosively.[9] Prior to rupture, the ovum and its surrounding granulosa cells (corona radiata) become detached from the follicle wall. At the time of rupture, there is an escape of antral fluid and the ovum exudes from the surface of the ovary to be transported to the ampulla by the fimbria of the oviduct. Following rupture, the follicle wall collapses resulting in hemorrhage into the theca interna. The stigma (point of follicle rupture) is sealed by a coagulum that is derived from blood and fibrin from the cavity of the follicle.

At the time of rupture, both the granulosa and theca interna cells undergo active mitosis with a rapid increase in cell numbers. Prior to ovulation, a network of capillaries is present in the theca interna but not in the granulosa layer where there is only a network of intercellular sinusoids (Cal-Exner spaces) that show an accumulation of follicular fluid. Following ovulation, as the corpus luteum is formed, capillaries sprout from the theca, invading the granulosa layer.[10,11] The granulosa cells continue to undergo hypertrophy and hyperplasia as the corpus luteum progressively increases in size for several days; enlargement continues for 2 to 8 days.[12,13] During this time, the theca cells (theca lutein) complete their division, lose coherence, and become grouped around the periphery of the granulosa layer, between the folds of the granulosa cells. The theca cells, and to a lesser extent the granulosa cells, show greatly increased metabolic activity including increased fat storage. If fertilization and implantation do not take place, degeneration occurs at about 9 days after ovulation. Subsequently granulosa cells lose their columnar arrangement and become vacuolated and granular. There is increased invasion of the luteal structure by connective tissue, including fibroblastic organization of the central coagulum and the granulosa layer. In about 3 months, the corpus luteum is transformed by hyalin degeneration into a corpus albicans.

If fertilization occurs, the ovum migrates to the uterine wall and may become implanted after 6 to 8 days. The cellular components of the corpus luteum undergo hypertrophy and hyperplasia, and during this time more estrogens and progestogens are produced.[14] Although the corpus luteum appears to be necessary for implantation, it is controversial whether it is required beyond the early stages for continuation of pregnancy. Morphologically, the corpus luteum persists until the end of pregnancy.

Luteolysis and uteroovarian relationships

Luteolysis is the process by which the corpus luteum loses its ability to secrete progesterone, eventually becoming transformed into a corpus albicans. Control of luteal function results from the production of a luteolytic hormone (luteolysin) in the endometrium, which is then transmitted through the uteroovarian circulation to the corpus luteum. Knowledge of the possibility that the endometrial luteolytic hormone exists resulted from experiments showing that the corpora lutea of guinea pigs persisted for a 2- to 3-month period following bilateral hysterectomy.[15] This was in contrast to a much shorter normal life-span of the guinea pig corpora lutea (14 to 16 days). These experiments also showed that the lengthening of the life-span of the corpora lutea was roughly proportional to the amount of uterine tissue eliminated. When only one uterine horn was removed,

the life-span of the corpora lutea was less than if both horns were excised.[16] Transplantation of homologous uterine tissue in hysterectomized hamsters greatly shortens the life of the corpora lutea as compared to that in hamsters with bilateral hysterectomies.[17]

Not all mammals demonstrate an increasing life-span of the corpus luteum following hysterectomy. Those mammals that react like the guinea pig include the pig, cow, sheep, and hamster. Mammals that show no change in the corpus luteum life-span following hysterectomy include the ferret, opossum, monkey, and human. In both the rat and the rabbit, the ovarian cycle is not altered by the removal of the uterine horns; however, if the female's hysterectomy follows mating, the period of pseudopregnancy is lengthened by several days.

Most experimental work in the human and the monkey has been unable to demonstrate an alteration of the life-span of the corpus luteum following hysterectomy. A study utilizing daily urinary pregnanediol analyses was performed on women with hysterectomy performed either on day 17 or 18 or on day 24 or 25 of the menstrual cycle.[18] In the former group, five of the six patients showed a prolonged luteal function, which in one case persisted until day 36. None of the women in the 24- and 25-day group showed an alteration of luteal function. Although other studies have been performed on humans or primates, they have not demonstrated that hysterectomy results in an alteration of corpus luteum function.

In those mammals in which corpus luteum function responds to hysterectomy, the increase in the life-span usually corresponds to the length of gestation. The corpus luteum life-span may be increased not only by hysterectomy but also by a ligature around the oviducts and the blood vessels that join the uterus to the ovary.[19] The instillation of alcohol solutions into the uterine lumen of the horn adjacent to the corpora lutea will increase the life-span of the unilateral corpora lutea. In contrast, when the uterine horns are distended by small plastic or glass beads, the life-span of the corpora lutea is shortened from the usual 16 or 17 days to 11 days in sheep, and from 15 or 16 days to about 12 days in the guinea pig. This shortening effect could be abolished in sheep by denervating the uterine segment containing the bead.

Experimental evidence suggests that luteolysin is produced in the endometrium during the luteal phase and is transported locally to the ovaries. When one uterine horn is distended in the guinea pig, only the corpora lutea on the distended side regress, while the corpora lutea on the non-distended side are not affected. In these guinea pigs, when a unilateral hysterectomy was performed, the corpora lutea in the side operated on were larger and persisted for longer periods of time; those on the other side regressed in the normal manner. Similar results have been noted in the pig.

Gonadal hormones (steroids)

All hormones thus far identified as secretory products of the gonads are steroids. The basic chemical component of the steroid structure is the perhydrocyclopentanophenanthrene structure, and steroids are derived from a methylated product of perhydrocyclopentanophenanthrene, sterane.

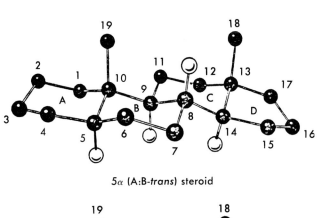

5α (A:B-*trans*) steroid

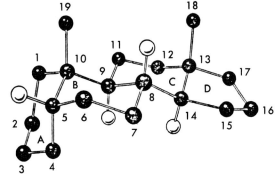

5β (A:B-*cis*) steroid

Fig. 3-5. Photographs of three-dimensional models of the steroid nucleus with 5α hydrogen (top) or 5β hydrogen (bottom). The ring structures are identified by the letters A, B, C, and D, and the carbon atoms by the numbers 1 to 17. Methyl groups are indicated at 18 and 19. (Modified with permission from Klyne, W.: Chemistry of the steroids, New York, 1957, John Wiley & Sons, Inc.)

Each carbon atom of this compound is designated by a number; the entire ring structure has 17 carbons. In a graphical depiction, the structural formula is usually abbreviated by designating each methyl group by a line and each carbon as an angle, as illustrated in Fig. 3-5. The two methyl groups shown are numbered 18 and 19. Additional side groups, attached to No. 17, are sequentially numbered 20, 21, 22, etc.

Adrenal steroid hormones. Cortisol and aldosterone are C-21 steroids (21 carbon atoms) and are derived from the pregnane series. The androgens are C-19 steroids, and the estrogens (that lack the C-19 methyl group) are C-18 steroids. Chemical names of the androgens are derived from the androstane basic structure; names of the estrogenic steroids are derived from the estrane basic structure. More common names are also applied to steroid hormones and are more frequently used in practice. Thus testosterone is, chemically, Δ^4,3-keto,17-hydroxyandrostene. The delta designation (Δ) describes the position of the double bond; androst*ene* signifies that this is an unsaturated compound as compared to the saturated ring structure androst*ane*.

Steroids in nature. The perhydrocyclopentanophenanthrene nucleus forms the basic structure of a large series of compounds found throughout the animal and plant kingdoms. Plants contain steroid compounds, some of which have estrogenic activity when administered to mammals. Vitamin D and the bile acids are steroids. Digitalis preparations, originally obtained from plants and used medically as cardiac glycosides, are also steroids. A variety of carcinogenic compounds are derived from phenanthrene. In addition, since there are so many functional steroid hormones in vertebrates, the spectrum of steroid activities in nature is almost unlimited.

Steroid structure. The steroid structure has thus far been presented as a two-dimensional figure; however, extremely important isomeric forms of steroids also exist. For example, there are asymmetrical centers in the testosterone molecule (carbon atoms 5, 8, 9, 10, 13, 14, 17); when additional side groupings are added, additional opportunities for asymmetry exist. Biologically active steroid hormones always contain the C and D rings in the same relative positions (*trans* position). However, the relationship of the A and B rings may differ. The relation of the A and B rings dictates the position of the hydrogen atom at carbon 5. This position is stated relative to the methyl group on carbon 10, which is assumed to lie above the plane of the molecule. If the hydrogen at 5 lies on the same side of the molecular plane as the methyl group, the A and B rings are *cis* to each other and the hydrogen is in the β position. If the hydrogen is opposite the methyl group of carbon 10, the A and B rings are *trans* to each other and the hydrogen is in the α position. Thus, the 5α or 5β position indicates more than merely a hydrogen position; it also reflects major isometric changes in the A and B ring relationships. (Fig. 3-5.) Hydroxyl groups at carbon 3 may also lie in either an α or a β position. Their positions are designated by a broken line for α, and a solid line for β.

Steroid synthesis. The precursors of adrenal, ovarian, and testicular hormones are cholesterol and acetate. The gland may metabolize cholesterol that is obtained from blood circulating through it or synthesize acetate (also obtained from blood or metabolism) into steroids. The pathways of synthesis common to testis and ovary are shown in Fig. 3-6. These pathways also exist within the adrenal cortex, but in addition the adrenal contains pathways directed to producing glucocorticoids such as cortisol and aldosterone. These pathways are not depicted in Fig. 3-6. The specific enzymes synthesizing the steroids are similar in the adrenal cortex, ovary, and testis. Biosynthetic routes of the granulosa cells seem to favor estradiol synthesis.

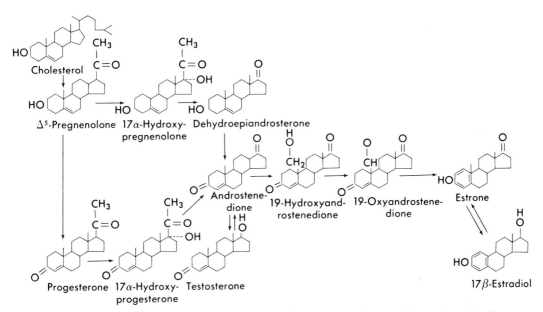

Fig. 3-6. Steroid biosynthetic pathway believed to exist in the ovaries and testes. The major hormonal secretory product of the testis is testosterone; the ovary secretes 17β-estradiol, progesterone, and 17α-hydroxyprogesterone. See text for details.

Those of the Leydig cells favor testosterone. Although testosterone is synthesized as a precursor of estradiol in the ovary, it is not secreted in large amounts. Furthermore, although testosterone may be metabolized to estradiol under some conditions by the testes, the bulk is secreted as testosterone. Testosterone production in women and estradiol production in men are discussed in greater detail in Chapters 5 and 6.

Congenital defects of steroid synthesis such as deficiency of 17-hydroxylase lead to synthetic defects in the ovary and adrenal cortex in women.[20] Cortisol and estradiol synthesis both require steroid precursors that are hydroxylated in the 17 position.

The first step in hormonal formation from cholesterol is the cleavage of the 22-to-27 side chain to form Δ^5-pregnenolone, which is subsequently transformed to progesterone.[21] The enzymes that degrade the cholesterol side chain, as well as the enzyme (3β-dehydrogenase) that transforms

pregnenolone to progesterone, are located within the mitochondria. Subsequently Δ^5-pregnenolone and progesterone are hydroxylated in the 17 position under the influence of 17-hydroxylase from the soluble fraction of the cytoplasm. Thus considerable transfer of substrates apparently occurs within the cell. Variations in enzyme concentrations within cells of different secreting glands determine the final products. The 20, 21 side chain of 17-hydroxyprogesterone and 17-hydroxypregnenolone is subsequently cleaved to form dehydroepiandrosterone and androstenedione, respectively. Dehydroepiandrosterone is rapidly transformed to androstenedione, and this steroid exists in equilibrium with testosterone. Conversion of androstenedione to estrone probably occurs by formation of 19-hydroxyandrostenedione. Finally aromatization of the A ring results in formation of estrone, which in turn is metabolized to 17β-estradiol. As was discussed earlier, different cell types appear to have preferential steroid syn-

29

thetic pathways—for example, the granulosa cell rapidly synthesizes testosterone and estradiol from acetate; the corpus luteum rapidly converts cholesterol or acetate to progesterone.

THE VAGINA

In the virginal state, the vagina is positioned with its walls in apposition, forming a potential cavity. The anterior wall ranges in length from 6 to 7.5 cm and the posterior wall is approximately 9 cm. The vaginal cavity is constricted at the introitus, dilated in the middle, and narrow near the uterine end. The uterine cervix projects into the vaginal cavity and the recess around the cervix (the fornix) is divided into anterior, posterior, and lateral sections.

Anatomical structure

The vagina is made up of three layers: epithelium, muscularis, and adventitial connective tissue. The epithelium is con-

tinuous with the cervical mucosa and the cutaneous epithelium of the labia. The muscularis consists of two layers: a strong external longitudinal layer, whose fibers are continuous with the uterine muscle fibers, and a weaker internal circular layer, where the vagina is surrounded by a band of striated muscle fibers called the bulbocavernosus. Adventitial connective tissue surrounds the muscularis and is contiguous with the connective tissues of the urinary bladder, rectum, and other pelvic structures.

Hormone stimulation of the vaginal mucosa

The vaginal mucosa responds to ovarian hormones by proliferation, differentiation, and desquamation of its cells (Fig. 3-7).[22] During prepubescence and late menopause, since minimal amounts of these hormones are present, an atrophic smear is produced that is devoid of superficial cells. In adults,

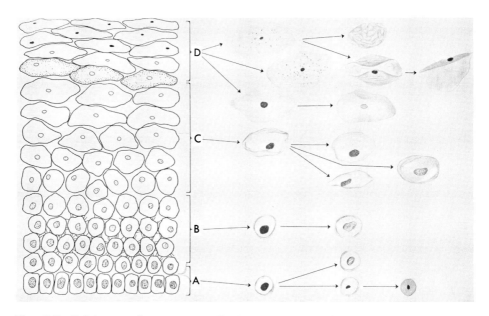

Fig. 3-7. Exfoliation of squamous cells from vaginal epithelium: *A,* basal layer; *B,* parabasal layer; *C,* intermediate layer; *D,* superficial layer. (Reprinted with permission from de Neef, J. C.: Clinical endrocrine cytology, New York, 1965, Hoeber Medical Division, Harper & Row, Publishers.)

the vaginal mucosa proliferates and differentiates in response to increasing amounts of estrogen during the proliferative phase and later undergoes desquamation when progesterone is added in the luteal phase. Exogenous administration of ovarian hormones produces the same effects as endogenous hormones if administered in suitable dosages.

Proliferation of the vaginal epithelium results from mitoses of the cells of the basal layer and culminates in an increased thickness of the vaginal epithelium, due to a progressive increase in the number of cells in the parabasal and intermediate layers. It is induced by various hormones, including estrogens, androgens, or progestogens. These hormones directly affect the epithelium, eliciting a cellular response that varies according to the potency of the hormone. Of all the naturally occurring steroid hormones, 17β-estradiol is one of the most effective.

Differentiation of the vaginal epithelium takes place in the parabasal and intermediate layers, with formation of intracytoplasmic glycogen. Terminal differentiation is characterized by appearance of cytoplasmic prekeratin granules in the superficial layer, with simultaneous diminution in the cell glycogen content. Stimulation of the vaginal cells by estrogens, progesterone, or testosterone results in formation of glycogen in the intermediate cells. However, only the estrogens have the ability to induce karyopyknosis and cornification, which complete the differentiation process in the superficial layer. Karyopyknosis refers to the shrinkage of the nucleus as the total nuclear volume decreases, eventually becoming pyknotic; cornification occurs in the cytoplasm, resulting in a pink coloration following staining with eosin dyes.

Desquamation may occur in both the superficial and intermediate layers, but only rarely in the parabasal layer. During desquamation, the cells may be released from the vaginal mucosa either in clusters or as isolated cells, and the exfoliated cells may be flat or folded. Progesterone exerts a strong desquamative effect on the superficial cells; less desquamation is evident following estrogen stimulation.

Under experimental conditions, where the combined activity of several hormones has been studied, progesterone is synergistic with estrogen during the phases of proliferation and differentiation of the intermediate layer; however, progesterone is antagonistic to estrogen in the differentiation of the superficial layer. Because of the marked desquamative properties of progesterone, the vaginal epithelial cells are desquamated before they are able to undergo complete differentiation. Testosterone is synergistic with estrogen in the process of proliferation and early differentiation in the intermediate layer. Testosterone never causes karyopyknosis or cornification when acting alone, and its differentiating effect is less than that of estrogen. The desquamating effect of testosterone is less than that of progesterone.

The vaginal epithelial cells vary in their response to ovarian hormones, depending on the anatomical site in the vaginal cavity. The distal portion of the vagina is the most sensitive to stimulation by the ovarian hormones. Although ectocervical and vaginal cells close to the introitus demonstrate an increasing amount of karyopyknosis following the administration of estrogens, this is not as great as the amount of karyopyknosis that takes place in the distal portion of the vagina. The response of the vaginal cells to either endogenous or exogenous estrogens may be affected by obesity, with increased storage of estrogens in the adipose tissue, and by hepatic, intestinal, and renal abnormalities—which may affect conjugation, absorption, or excretion of the steroids. In addition, local factors such as trichomonad infestation, bacterial infection with or without ulcerations, vaginal jellies and douches, prolapse with leukoplakia, and mechanical irritation from a pessary may influence the eosinophilia of vaginal superficial cells; therefore this eosinophilia is not as reliable an indicator as karyopyknosis.

THE CERVIX

The cervix measures approximately 2 to 4 cm in length and is continuous with the inferior portion of the body of the uterus. The bulk of the cervix is composed of connective tissue with scattered smooth muscle fibers. It projects into the upper vaginal cavity for a distance of approximately 1 to 2 cm, and the anterior and posterior lips surround the external cervical os. A central orifice (the endocervical canal) communicates with the vaginal cavity through the external cervical os and enters the uterine cavity at the inner cervical os. The endocervical canal serves to transport sperm into the uterine cavity; and at the time of delivery, it becomes greatly enlarged and dilated to facilitate passage for the fetus.

The mucosa

Layers of squamous cells, which are continuous from the vaginal mucosa, cover the vaginal portion of the cervix. These cells respond to ovarian hormones as the squamous cells of the vagina do; however, they do not show the quantitative responses normally seen in the posterior and lateral aspects of the vaginal mucosa. Glycogen is present in the cytoplasm of the squamous cells of the intermediate zone in most areas of the cervical epithelium. Keratin may be seen on the squamous epithelial surface although keratinization is not as prominent as it is in the vagina. The squamocolumnar junction is an abrupt transition between the squamous cells that are derived from the vaginal portion of the cervix and the columnar cells of the endocervical canal. In the nonpregnant woman of child-bearing age, this junction lies close to the external os. In the pregnant woman, the lips of the cervix are everted and the junction is displaced laterally. In the menopausal woman, the squamocolumnar junction retracts up into the endocervical canal, where it is not readily accessible for biopsy.

The epithelium of the endocervical canal is characterized by tall, secretory columnar cells. Cell height and the amount of secretions of the endocervical cells are cyclical and vary according to stimulation by the ovarian hormones.[23] The height of the cells is greatest at the time of ovulation when the amount of circulating estrogen is highest. Under the influence of estrogen, the endocervical cell accumulates columns of mucus at its apical end; after ovulation, large portions of the cell are sloughed off into the gland duct. Each wave of estrogen secretion causes an accumulation and storage of mucus followed by the sloughing of a portion of endocervical cell. It has been shown that the mucus-secreting cells are rich in glycogen and glycoprotein and contain large amounts of mucopolysaccharides. Ciliated cells are present in the endocervix but in smaller quantities than the secretory cells. The endocervical glands (racemose glands) are made up of numerous branching ducts which end in acini. The number of cells in these glands increases during pregnancy, and during menopause they become fewer in number and atrophic.

Cervical mucus

At the time of ovulation, the cervical mucus is most copious and the viscosity is markedly decreased (Fig. 3-8).[24] In contrast, during the preovulatory and postovulatory periods the amount is sparse and the mucus is of high viscosity. In both of these phases, the wet weight of the mucus contains 92% to 94% water; the water content rises to 98% at the time of ovulation. At the time of ovulation, the sodium chloride content of cervical mucus rises to 40% to 70% as compared with 2% to 20% during the preovulatory and postovulatory phases.

Cervical mucus consists of mucoid substances of epithelial origin, which are com-

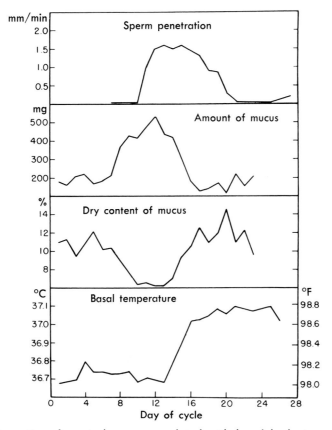

Fig. 3-8. Properties of cervical mucus correlated with basal body temperature during one menstrual cycle. (Reprinted with permission from Bishop, D. W.: In Young, W. C., editor: Sex and internal secretions, vol. 2, ed. 3, Baltimore, 1961, The Williams & Wilkins Co.)

posed of glycoproteins predominantly of the sialomucin type.[25] These glycoproteins contain approximately 75% carbohydrates and 25% amino acids. The structure of mucin is believed to consist of a long, continuous polypeptide chain with numerous oligosaccharide side chains. Galactose, glucosamine, fucose, and sialic acid comprise the majority of the carbohydrate portion.

The glycoprotein filaments are oriented so that the spaces between the filaments measure 2 to 5 μ while under the influence of estrogens; the spaces in the meshwork of filaments have a smaller diameter in the luteal phase, when meshes range from 0.5 to 2.2 μ. Because the size of the meshes is greater around the time of ovulation, sperm pass freely through the meshwork of filaments and through the endocervical canal, which is not possible during the luteal phase.

The soluble protein concentration varies between 0.4 and 4 grams/100 ml. Most of the proteins have been identified as serum proteins and include prealbumin, lipoprotein, albumin, and beta and gamma globulins. It is doubtful that the ovarian hormones alter the quality of the serum proteins, although changes in quantitative composition occur during the menstrual cycle. Numerous enzymes have been de-

33

tected in cervical mucus, including acid phosphatase, alkaline phosphatase, β-glucuronidase, amylase, phosphorylase, and esterase. Lysozyme is present in cervical mucus as well as many other body secretions. Its action results in a nonspecific defense mechanism against bacterial infections.

Through the technique of sulfur 35 uptake by connective tissue it has been demonstrated that this isotope is taken up rapidly by the connective tissue of the cervix during the first half of the cycle, with a precipitous drop during the early luteal phase, followed by a rapid rise to the preovulatory levels during the late portion of the luteal phase.[26] Within the collagen fibers of the cervix, the sulfur 35 is synthesized into chondroitin sulfate, which participates in the formation of the interfibrillar bridges to bind collagen fibrils into collagen bundles. It is thought that the rapid chondroitin sulfate synthesis is related to constriction of the cervix during preovulatory and postovulatory phases and decreased synthesis with dilation of the cervix at midcycle.

THE UTERUS
Anatomical structure

The uterus (Fig. 3-1) is a muscular organ situated between the urinary bladder and the rectum. It is triangular in shape and, in women of child-bearing age, measures 6.5 to 8 cm in length, 2.5 to 3 cm in thickness and 5 to 6 cm in width at the fundus, and 2.5 to 3 cm in width at the isthmus. The body of the uterus is continuous with the cervix and is joined by the oviducts at the lateral sides of the fundus. The anterior and posterior uterine surfaces are apposed and the endometrial surfaces are in juxtaposition, making the interior of the uterus a potential cavity. The lower part of the uterine cavity is also continuous with the endocervical canal and the lumina of the oviducts above. The external surface, which is covered by serosa, is continuous with the folds over the urinary bladder and rectum. The interior of the uterus is lined with a mucosal surface called the endometrium. Beneath this layer lies the myometrium, composed of three indistinct layers of smooth muscles, which interlace and are held in position by connective tissue with elastic fibers. The outer layer consists of longitudinal fibers that are continuous with those of the broad and round ligaments. The middle muscular layer makes up the major portion of the myometrium. The inner muscular layer is composed of thin strands arranged longitudinally and obliquely. Blood vessels between the muscle fibers are so situated that they may be obstructed following the delivery of an infant. A system of helically coiled collagen fibers interwoven throughout the endometrial stroma may branch or anastomose with fibers of an adjoining collagen fiber helix.

Blood supply

Blood is supplied to the uterus by uterine and ovarian arteries. On both sides of the uterus, the uterine artery gives off right-angle branches termed radial arteries. Within the myometrium, the radial arteries again branch—into straight arteries and more radial arteries, which in turn branch into straight or coiled arteries. The coiled arteries extend through the inner myometrium and the thickness of the endometrium, eventually dividing to give rise to the capillaries in the superficial endometrium. Capillary plexuses are formed in the stroma and around the endometrial glands. These plexuses and sinusoidal vascular lakes drain most of the endometrium; blood is returned to the collecting veins in the myometrium and then to the main uterine veins along the lateral surface of the uterus. The straight arteries terminate in capillaries in the basilar layer of the endometrium and support regeneration of the lower portion of the functional layer of endometrium. The coiled arteries supply blood to the middle portion and a superficial portion of endometrium. The coiled arteries are most responsive to cyclical changes in the estrogen and progesterone levels. Since the vascular pattern is constantly changing with proliferation and regression, several straight arteries may at times become coiled, and they may subsequently regress to the straight variety.

The endometrium

The endometrial tissue and its secretions play a major role in the reproductive process. As spermatozoa pass through the intrauterine cavity to the oviducts, they are bathed in endometrial secretions. As the fertilized ovum is transported to the uterine cavity, it receives nutrients from the uterine secretions during the days before implantation. Following implantation, the embryo depends upon an adequate vascular supply within the endometrium. Thereafter, physiological properties of the endometrium and its blood supply are key factors in survival and growth of the embryo throughout gestation.

The endometrium is selectively responsive to the ovarian hormones estrogen and progesterone. These hormones must be secreted cyclically and with an optimal quantitative ratio of estrogen to progesterone in order to produce maximal growth and maturation of the endometrial tissue.[27] Their mechanism of action is discussed in Chapter 5.

THE MENSTRUAL CYCLE

The cyclical changes of the endometrium in the normally ovulating and menstruating woman occur in a slow transitional process (Fig. 3-9).[28,29] The first half of the cycle (proliferative phase) begins at the end of menstruation and ends at the time of ovulation. During this phase, proliferation of glandular and superficial epithelium, stroma, and blood vessels takes place under the effect of estrogens. Following ovulation, maturation of the stroma and glands takes place under the continuing influence of estrogen with the addition of progesterone. This is known as the luteal phase, which begins at the time of ovulation and extends to the beginning of menstruation. Menstruation ensues and establishes day one of the next cycle as the first day of menstruation. The luteal phase is generally a more constant period, usually being 14 ± 2 days.

The proliferative phase

In the first part of the cycle, proliferation occurs in the glands, stroma, blood vessels, and superficial epithelium. The thickness of the endometrium may have reached a height of approximately 1 mm during the early proliferative stage and from 3 to 5 mm at the time of ovulation. In the early proliferative endometrium, the superficial epithelium is thin, the glands are sparse and nontortuous, and the lumina are narrow. Only occasional mi-

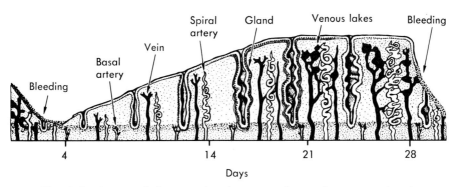

Fig. 3-9. Structural changes of endometrium during the menstrual cycle.

toses are seen in either the glands or the stroma, and there is a minimal amount of pseudostratification of gland nuclei. As proliferation continues, the glands become more tortuous and stromal edema is prominent. An increasing number of mitoses are seen in both the glands and the stroma. In the late proliferative phase, the superficial and glandular epithelium becomes pseudostratified. The glands are more tortuous, containing a moderate number of mitoses, and the stromal cells are greatly increased in number.

Ovulation and the luteal phase

Histological changes specific for ovulation are not seen until approximately 36 hours following ovulation. At this time, the earliest indications of ovulation are subnuclear glycogen-containing vacuoles that develop between the nuclei of the glandular cells and the basement membrane. These vacuoles increase in number so that approximately 48 hours after ovulation, most glandular cells in the functional portion of the endometrium have a subnuclear vacuole. The glands continue to increase in tortuosity and the pseudostratification of the nuclei remains for several days. As the glands mature, the nuclei become arranged in a single row above their corresponding subnuclear vacuoles. At 4 or 5 days after ovulation, the subnuclear vacuoles migrate around the nucleus with a corresponding nuclear movement toward the base of the cell. At approximately the sixth day following ovulation, secretion in the gland lumen is maximal and fluid accumulates in the stroma. At this time, the apical tufts of the gland cells separate from the remainder of the cell and are mixed with the intraluminal gland content. From the sixth postovulatory day to the time of menstruation, the glands show marked tortuosity and maximal secretion into the lumina. At the time of implantation of the ovum, the stroma is loose and edematous, facilitating penetration by the trophoblast.

On the eighth or ninth postovulatory day, an early predecidual reaction develops in the periarteriolar cells of the stroma. Stromal edema decreases and the predecidual reaction extends into adjoining portions of the stroma; the glandular secretion is still active but subsiding. By the eleventh and twelfth postovulatory days, virtually all of the stromal cells in the functional layer of endometrium show a predecidual reaction, and lymphocytes invade the stroma and increase in proportion to the quantity of the predecidual reaction. Stromal mitoses are seen during the last 4 days of the cycle. If implantation does not occur, polymorphonuclear leukocytes migrate into the stroma on the thirteenth and fourteenth postovulatory days as the endometrial tissue prepares for menstruation.

Menstruation and endometrial blood supply

The blood supply to the endometrium increases progressively during the menstrual cycle.[30] The straight arteries, which arise from the arcuate vessels of the myometrium, supply the basal portion of the endometrium. These vessels are not greatly affected by estrogen and progesterone; consequently they aid in the regeneration of endometrial tissue after menstruation. In contrast, the spiral arteries of the endometrium are markedly influenced by estrogen and progesterone; they grow rapidly following stimulation by estrogen during the proliferative phase and their walls become thicker during the latter half of the cycle. Elastic fibrils present in the media and adventitia allow the spiral arteries to change length and diameter with greater rapidity than the straight arteries can. During the luteal phase of the cycle, the spiral arteries become coiled as they outgrow the thickness of the endometrium.

In experiments in which monkey endometrium was transplanted to the anterior chamber of the eye, the morphological events taking place at menstruation could be seen with the naked eye.[31] In these endometrial transplants, the tissue regressed and bled at each menstrual period. The spiral arteries underwent a considerable amount of constriction at the time of estrogen-progesterone withdrawal, which was followed by dilation of the arteries. Blood flow through the capillaries diminished sharply and the number of capillaries available for supplying blood to the stroma decreased significantly. The stroma consequently became more dense and the coiled arteries became bent and collapsed, resulting in an obstruction of blood flow. Decreased oxygenation of the endometrial tissues and consequent degeneration of the surrounding stroma ensued following blood stasis. Constriction of the spiral arteries, which occurred from 4 to 24 hours before the time of visible bleeding, usually began in one artery and then developed in others. Bleeding continued as long as there was arterial blood flow; eventually the small hemorrhages became confluent and the majority of endometrial tissue was sloughed.

Endometrial fluid

Morphological changes of the glands and stroma are associated with equally marked changes in chemical composition in the biochemical substances. Water content of the endometrial tissues ranges from 80% to 83% of the dry weight during the proliferative phase and from 78% to 84% during the luteal phase. Most of the water is found in the stromal tissues. The electrolytes potassium, sodium, and chloride vary only slightly during the cycle.[32,33] One of the most important metabolites in the endometrium is glucose, which cannot be utilized in the free form but must undergo phosphorylation in the plasma membrane of the gland cells.[34] As a result of this reaction, glucose-6-phosphate is formed by the enzyme hexokinase. This intermediate, glucose-6-phosphate, becomes the basic energy substance in the cytoplasm of the endometrial cells. In this form, it may be polymerized and stored as glycogen, or it may be utilized for energy either anaerobically or aerobically. During anaerobic metabolism, glucose is broken down to pyruvate and finally to lactic acid. During aerobic metabolism, glucose-6-phosphate is reduced to pyruvic acid which is subsequently oxidized through the Krebs citric acid cycle. In addition, glucose-6-phosphate may be metabolized into pentose phosphate intermediates that may in turn be utilized as a source of ribose and other sugars having 4, 5, or 7 carbons. To provide glucose for uterine fluid, the glucose-6-phosphate may be hydrolyzed by the enzyme glucose-6-phosphatase to yield glucose. Nutrients for migrating sperm and the blastocyst are provided in this manner.

The glycogen content in the endometrium increases progressively until the fifth or sixth day following ovulation and then decreases in amount until menstruation. When glycogen in the endometrial tissue attains a level of 500 to 700 mg/100 grams, wet weight, it is usually converted to glucose. Throughout the menstrual cycle, the level of glucose in tissue remains relatively constant, usually between 40 and 60 mg/100 grams, wet weight; this amount is approximately one half of that found in blood. Maximal conversion of glycogen to glucose occurs at the time of ovulation, and glucose is then secreted into the gland lumen for several days. At this same time there is a high glucose content in both the uterine secretions and the cervical mucus.

Histochemical studies of the endometrium have shown that glycogen in the form of small granules is present at the base of the glandular cells; as the cells enlarge during the proliferative phase, the granules increase in number in the basal portion of the cell, pushing the nucleus toward the middle of the cell. After ovulation, these glycogen granules migrate to a supranuclear location and are released during the early luteal phase.

Alkaline phosphatase is an enzyme present in the endometrium. Because of its location in the plasma membrane it plays an important role in transport of biochemical substances across the membrane. It may also be active in metabolism of glycogen. This enzyme is present in the stromal cells following menstruation and participates in regeneration of the endometrium. During the early proliferative phase, alkaline phosphatase is found in the glandular epithelium and smaller amounts are present in the endothelial cells of the spiral arterioles. Around the time of ovulation, it is seen in increasing concentrations in the plasma membrane of the glands and is presumably involved in the active transport of glucose and glycogen into the gland lumen. Following ovulation, much of the enzyme is seen in the lumen, although a smaller amount is still present on the surface of the gland cells. In the luteal phase, alkaline phosphatase is localized in the endothelium of the spiral arterioles in increasing quantities.

Acid phosphatase is located in the cytoplasm close to the plasma membrane of the gland cells, although smaller amounts are also present in the stromal cells. This enzyme is present mainly during the luteal phase, increasing in quantity from the time of ovulation to the premenstrual phase. Acid phosphatase and other proteolytic enzymes are located in cytoplasmic structures called lysosomes. These lysosomes detoxify the toxic substances that accumulate within the cells. Around the time of menses the enzymes are released from the lysosomes, diffusing throughout the cytoplasm, and the destructive capabilities of these enzymes ultimately cause death of the cell.

The protein content of the uterine secretions varies both qualitatively and quantitatively during the menstrual cycle and early implantation. The protein concentration in uterine fluid is two to three times higher during the luteal phase than in the ovulatory phase. In both the rabbit and the ferret, the protein concentration in the uterine fluid increases at the time of implantation as well as in the luteal phase of the cycle. The uterine proteins include albumin, uteroglobulin, transferrin, beta globulins, and gamma globulins. An iron-binding protein, lactoferrin, is located in gland cells and has antimicrobial properties.[35] In addition, it may function to exchange iron between the mother and the fetus. Lactoferrin is found in relatively low amounts during the proliferative phase and is markedly increased during the late luteal phase. A protein called blastokinin is found in the uterine fluid of several mammals, occurring several days before and after implantation. In the rabbit, RNA and protein synthesis of the blastocyst is accelerated by approximately 50% in the presence of blastokinin.[36] This substance also stimulates mitoses in the blastocysts of other mammals.

THE OVIDUCTS (FALLOPIAN TUBES)

The oviducts, each measuring 10 to 13 cm in length and 0.5 to 1.2 cm in diameter, arise from the fundus on the lateral sides of the uterus and extend to the ovaries. Each consists of an outer serosal surface surrounding three muscular layers (Fig. 3-10).[37] Lining the lumen of the oviduct is a mucosal layer that forms many papillary excrescences projecting into the lumen. The subperitoneal muscular layer extends longitudinally along the oviduct and continues into the fimbriae, forming a forklike enclosure at the upper and lower tubal edges. These fibers are anchored to the subperitoneal blood vessel fibers at the neck of the infundibulum. The middle muscular layer consists of fibers that parallel the blood vessels which encircle the tube. The inner muscular layer is arranged in spirals that intersect at regular intervals and end at the infundibulum where they intertwine with the circular fibers of the middle layer. The base of the infundibulum

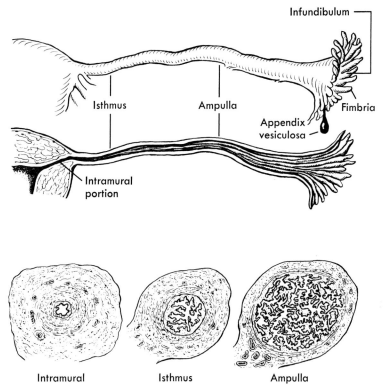

Fig. 3-10. Human oviduct (fallopian tube), gross and microscopic.

forms a functional sphincter by powerful musculature which is well vascularized.

The mucosal layer is comprised of epithelium and connective tissue. Characteristic mucosal folds in the ampullary portion of the oviduct are seen in a cross section of the oviduct, and these folds increase the surface area of the lumen markedly. Thus the number of cells available for fluid secretion into the lumen is greatly increased. Just as the lumen of the oviduct becomes larger approaching the fimbriated end, there are increased numbers of papillary excrescences. Both the diameter of the lumen and the number of papillary folds are markedly decreased in the isthmic portion of the oviduct. The epithelium is composed of columnar cells—both ciliated and secretory nonciliated cells. A third type of cell has been identified and is known as a peg cell or an intercalary cell. These are small cells that lack cytoplasmic material;

it is likely that they are secretory cells which have already extruded their cytoplasmic components into the lumen. They are most prominent during the premenstrual and menstrual phases. The epithelial cells respond to exogenous hormones by changes in size and cytoplasmic content. During estrogen stimulation in the proliferative phase, there is an increase in the number of ciliated and nonciliated cells. As estrogen stimulation progresses, the ciliated and the secretory cells enlarge and the number of organelles in the cytoplasm increases. During the late secretory phase, the number of secretory cells is greatly increased while the ciliated cells decrease. Histochemical studies have shown that PAS-positive material representing glycogen and glycoprotein is present in the cytoplasm surrounding the ciliated cell nucleus. Large amounts of PAS-positive material, which have been found in the fluid of the oviducts in the midluteal phase, are available to nourish the ovum during the preimplantation stage of development.

Anatomical structure

The oviduct may be divided lengthwise into four anatomical portions. First is the intramural portion, which has a narrow lumen and lies within the musculature of the myometrium extending from the uterine cavity to the serosal surface of the uterus. The muscle fibers surrounding this portion extend into the adjoining segment, the isthmus. The second portion of the oviduct, the isthmus, begins at the serosa of the uterus and extends approximately 2 cm where it terminates at the isthmic-ampullary junction. This portion, which is a straight thick muscular wall, has a relatively narrow luminal diameter that increases near the ampullary-isthmic junction. The longest of the four segments, the ampullary portion, is slightly convoluted and has a relatively thin muscular wall. Within this segment are the numerous papillary folds of epithelium. The last and most distal portion of the oviduct is the infundibular portion. Numerous delicate fimbriae covered with epithelium extend from the base of the infundibulum over part of the ovary at the time of ovulation; these fimbriae guide the ovum into the ampulla from the surface of the ovary. At the base of the infundibulum one of the folds, which is attached to the upper pole of the ovary, contains a muscle that functions by bringing the fimbriated ends of the infundibulum closer to the surface of the ovary during ovulation.

Muscular movements of the oviducts have been noted in the human as well as in many other species at the time of ovulation.[9,38] In the human, both the ovary and the fimbria are drawn closer to the uterus into a fossa on the posterior aspect of the broad ligament. These fimbriae form a cone over the ovarian surface, although at times the formation may not be directly over the

rupturing follicle. It has been shown that a current of fluid is present, which arises from the cul-de-sac and travels through the oviduct into the uterus. This may be a result of ciliary action lining the fimbria and epithelial surface of the oviduct.

Oviductal fluid

The oviducts secrete fluid against a pressure gradient, and the administration of pilocarpine increases the secretion pressure. The constituents of oviductal fluid have been measured in a number of mammals; however, no data are present for humans except in patients with hydrosalpinx.[39] Electrolyte concentrations are similar in both rabbit and monkey except for a somewhat higher concentration of sodium in the monkey. Sodium is the main cation and chloride the main anion of oviductal fluid, and both are present in higher quantities in this fluid than in blood. During the postovulatory period, minor variations occur in the electrolyte pattern which show an increase in the concentration of calcium and a decrease in sodium. Both sodium and chloride are decreased in concentration when the level of endogenous estrogen is lowest. The amount of protein in oviductal fluid appears to be highest following the stimulation of both estrogen and progesterone and, in the case of the monkey, appears to be highest at the time of ovulation and in the immediate postovulatory period. Glucose is present in small quantities (1.6 to 3.6 mg/100 ml). The human oviductal epithelium utilizes the glycolytic pathway of metabolism, and lactic acid is produced in the oviductal epithelium. A probable source of energy for spermatozoa is the lactate found in this fluid; however, phospholipid may be an additional source. Lactic acid ranges from 10 to 84 mg/ml and is increased during the first 3 days of pregnancy in the rabbit. Bicarbonate concentration, which ranges from 1.1 to 2.2 mg/ml, increases following stimulation by estrogen, probably related to increasing carbonic anhydrase activity in the oviduct. The bicarbonate ion has been shown to stimulate oxygen uptake by mammalian spermatozoa. Both lactic acid and bicarbonate are important in the cleavage of fertilized ova.

REFERENCES

1. Delson, B., Lubin, S., and Reynolds, S. R. M.: Vascular patterns in the human ovary, Amer. J. Obstet. Gynec. **57**:842, 1949.
2. McKay, D. G., Hertig, A. T., Adams, E. C., and Danziger, S.: Histochemical observations on the germ cells of human embryos, Anat. Rec. **117**:201, 1953.
3. Zuckerman, S.: The number of oocytes in the mature ovary, Recent Progr. Hormone Res. **6**:63, 1951.
4. Block E.: Quantitative morphological investigations of the follicular system in women, Acta Anat. **14**:108, 1952.
5. Mandl, A. M., and Zuckerman, S.: Growth of oocyte and follicle in adult rat, J. Endocr. **8**:126, 1952.
6. Hertig, A. T.: The primary human oocyte: some observations on the fine structure of Balbiani's vitelline body and the origin of the annulate lamellae, Amer. J. Anat. **122**:107, 1968.
7. Hisaw, F. L.: Development of the graafian follicle and ovulation, Physiol. Rev. **27**:95, 1947.
8. Zachariae, F.: Studies on the mechanism of ovulation. Autoradiographic investigations on the uptake of radioactive sulphate (^{35}S) into the ovarian follicular mucopolysaccharides, Acta Endocr. **26**:215, 1957.
9. Decker, A.: Culdoscopic observations on the tubo-ovarian mechanism of ovum reception, Fertil. Steril. **2**:253, 1951.
10. Corner, G. W., Jr.: The histological dating of the human corpus luteum of menstruation, Amer. J. Anat. **98**:377, 1956.
11. Corner, G. W.: Development, organization and breakdown of the corpus luteum in the rhesus monkey, Contrib. Embryol. (Nos. 198-206) **31**:117, 1945.
12. Adams, E. C., and Hertig, A. T.: Studies on the human corpus luteum. I. Observations on the ultrastructure of development and regression of the luteal cells during the menstrual cycle, J. Cell Biol. **41**:696, 1969.
13. Adams, E. C., and Hertig, A. T.: Studies on the human corpus luteum. II. Observations on the ultrastructure of luteal cells during pregnancy, J. Cell Biol. **41**:716, 1969.
14. White, R. F., Hertig, A. T., Rock, J., and Adams, E.: Histological and histochemical observations on the corpus luteum of human pregnancy with special reference to corpora lutea associated with normal and abnormal ova, Contrib. Embryol. **34**:55, 1951.
15. Loeb, L.: The effect of extirpation of the uterus on the life and function of the corpus luteum in the guinea pig, Proc. Soc. Exp. Biol. Med. **20**:441, 1923.
16. Duby, R. T., McDaniel, J. W., Spilman, C. H., and Black, D. L.: Utero-ovarian relationships in the golden hamster. II. Quantitative and local influences of the uterus on ovarian function, Acta Endocr. **60**:603, 1969.
17. Caldwell, B. V., Mazer, R. S., and Wright, P. A.: Luteolysis as affected by uterine transplantation in the Syrian hamster, Endocrinology **80**:477, 1967.
18. Andreoli, C.: Corpus luteum activity after hysterectomy in women, Acta Endocr. **50**:65, 1965.
19. Clemens, J. A., Minaguchi, H., and Meites, J.: Relation of local circulation between ovaries and uterus to lifespan of corpora lutea in rats, Proc. Soc. Exp. Biol. Med. **127**:1248, 1968.
20. Axelrod, L. R., and Goldzieher, J. W.: The polycystic ovary. III. Steroid biosynthesis in normal and polycystic ovarian tissue, J. Clin. Endocr. **22**:431, 1962.
21. Ryan, K. J., and Smith, O. W.: Biogenesis of steroid hormones in the human ovary, Recent Progr. Hormone Res. **21**:367, 1965.
22. Papanicolaou, G. N.: The sexual cycle in the human female as revealed by vaginal smears, Amer. J. Anat. **52**(supp.):519, 1933.
23. Hamilton, C. E.: Observations on the cervical mucosa of the rhesus monkey, Contrib. Embryol. **33**:81, 1949.
24. Vickery, B. H., and Bennett, J. P.: The cervix and its secretion in mammals, Physiol. Rev. **48**:135, 1968.
25. Davajan, V., Nakamura, R. M., and Kharma, K.: Review: spermatozoan transport in cervical mucus, Obstet. Gynec. Survey **25**:1, 1970.
26. Stevens, V. C., Dickey, R. P., Vorys, N., Denko, C., and Ullery, J. C.: Synthesis of chondroitin sulfate by the human cervix during the menstrual cycle, Amer. J. Obstet. Gynec. **95**:959, 1966.
27. Good, R. G., and Moyer, D. L.: Estrogen-progesterone relationships in the development of secretory epithelium, Fertil. Steril. **19**:37, 1968.
28. Corner, G. W., and Hartman, C. G.: Cyclic changes in the endometrium of the rhesus monkey (Macaca mulatta), Contrib. Embryol. **34**:101, 1951.
29. Noyes, R. W., Hertig, A. T., and Rock, J.:

Dating the endometrial biopsy, Fertil. Steril. **1**:3, 1950.

30. Greiss, F. C., Jr., and Anderson, S. G.: Uterine vascular changes during the ovarian cycle, Amer. J. Obstet. Gynec. **103**:629, 1969.

31. Markee, J. E.: Menstruation in intraocular endometrial transplants in the rhesus monkey, Contrib. Embryol. **28**:219, 1940.

32. Daniel, E. E., and Boyes, D. A.: The electrolytes of the human uterus and their possible relation to functional activity, Amer. J. Obstet. Gynec. **73**:392, 1957.

33. Howard, E., and DeFeo, V. J.: Potassium and sodium content of uterine and seminal vesicle secretions, Amer. J. Physiol. **195**:65, 1959.

34. Hughes, E. C., Jacobs, R. D., Rubulus, A., and Husney, R. M.: Carbohydrate pathways of the endometrium, Amer. J. Obstet. Gynec. **85**:594, 1963.

35. Masson, P. L., Heremans, J. F., and Ferin, J.: Presence of an iron-binding protein (lactoferrin) in the genital tract of the human female. I. Its immunohistochemical localization in the endometrium, Fertil. Steril. **19**:679, 1968.

36. Krishnan, R. S., and Daniel, J. C., Jr.: "Blastokinin": inducer and regulator of blastocyst development in the rabbit uterus, Science **158**:490, 1967.

37. Mastroianni, L., Jr.: The structure and function of the fallopian tube, Clin. Obstet. Gynec. **5**:781, 1962.

38. Doyle, J. B.: Exploratory culdotomy for observation of tubo-ovarian physiology at ovulation time, Fertil. Steril. **2**:475, 1951.

39. David, A., Garcia, C. R., and Czernobilsky, B.: Human hydrosalpinx. Histologic study and chemical composition of fluid, Amer. J. Obstet. Gynec. **105**:400, 1969.

ADDITIONAL READINGS

DeAllende, I. L. C., and Orias, O.: Cytology of the human vagina, New York, 1950, Paul B. Hoeber, Inc.

Grady, H. G., and Smith, D. E., editors: The ovary, Baltimore, 1963, The Williams & Wilkins Co.

Hartman, C. G., and Leathem, J. H.: Oogenesis and ovulation. In Hartman, C. G., editor: Mechanisms concerned with conception, New York, 1963, The Macmillan Co.

Klyne, W.: The chemistry of the steroids, New York, 1957, John Wiley & Sons, Inc.

Schmidt-Matthiesen, H.: The normal human endometrium, New York, 1963, McGraw-Hill Book Co.

CHAPTER 4

The testis and the male sex accessories

THE TESTIS

The testis has two separate but related functions in reproduction: (1) production and storage of viable spermatozoa and (2) manufacture and secretion of androgens. Sperm produced by the testis are transported to a ductal system, located within the scrotal sac, which is necessary for transport, storage, and further maturation. Spermatozoa thus produced and nurtured must not only have the ability to transport their genetic material through the female genital tract, but also must have the underlying capabilities for ovum fertilization at the proper time and place in order to reproduce the species. The structure and functions of the testis are governed primarily by the gonadotropic hormones in addition to local cellular influences and environmental conditions.

Anatomical considerations

The testes are bilateral organs—one usually larger than the other. Each is an ovoid body, measuring approximately 4 to 5 cm in length and 2 to 3 cm in diameter, and is covered by a fibrous capsule called the tunica albuginea. The testicular mass is composed predominantly of the seminiferous tubules (Fig. 4-1). These tubules range from about 0.12 to 0.3 mm in diameter. The convoluted seminiferous tubules are characterized by multiple branching loops that form a completely closed anastomosing pattern similar to a spider's web.[1] Usually four but at times up to ten tubules join the rete testis in one segment of this anastomosing pattern. A rete testis is comprised of a network of thin tubules into which the seminiferous tubules drain and which themselves drain into the epididymis. In man, the tubules in one segment usually join those in another; the majority of the connections take place at the base of the segments. In contrast, in the rat a single tubule drains at both ends into the rete testis. None of the tubules end blindly in man, although diverticula are present measuring 1 to 2 mm in length. Joining the convoluted seminiferous tubules at their proximal ends are the tubuli recti, which are unbranched for the first 4 to 14 cm in length. Spermatogenic cells are present throughout the length of the tubules, and no histological differences have been noted except in the proximal portions joining the rete testis. Smooth muscle cells having contractile properties surround the seminiferous tubules.[2,3] Pulsations have been noted in freshly excised tubules; the nonmotile spermatozoa are actively transported through the tubules by this means.

The interstitial (Leydig) cells are located between the seminiferous tubules, together with numerous collagen fibers and abundant blood vessels and lymphatics. The interstitial cells produce testosterone and undergo cellular changes in response to LH and HCG. The cells, which comprise an unusual type of endocrine gland, develop from mesenchymal stroma (rather than an epithelial surface) and are scattered singly or in groups throughout the testicular nontubular mass.

Both testes are contained outside of the body cavity in a thin sac (scrotum) composed of skin, an incomplete layer of

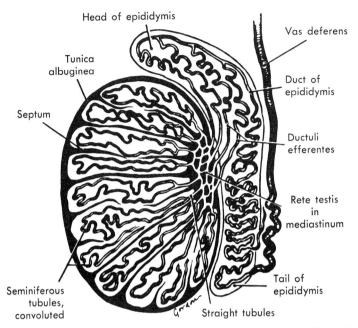

Fig. 4-1. Diagram showing the parts of the testis and the epididymis. (From Ham, A. W.: Histology, ed. 6, Philadelphia, 1969, J. B. Lippincott Co.)

smooth muscle (dartos layer), and some subcutaneous tissue. The surface area of the scrotum is considerable, permitting heat loss and maintenance at a temperature slightly below that of the body cavity. The dartos muscle contracts in response to cold, making the scrotum smaller and the wall corrugated, thus drawing the testes closer to the body. On the posterior border of each organ, the tunica is greatly thickened and extends into the testis for a short distance, forming an incomplete septum called the mediastinum. In the mediastinum of each testis is a network of ducts (the rete testis) lined with epithelium. The anastomotic network of seminiferous tubules ends in the tubuli recti, which in turn empty into the ducts of the rete testis. On the external surface of each testis is an elongated cylindrical structure, the epididymis, which extends from the upper pole across the posterolateral surface of the testis. The proximal portion (head) of the epididymis contains the convoluted ductuli efferentes as

they emerge from the rete testis. The multiple ductules combine into one long tube in the epididymis, which assumes an extremely tortuous convoluted course in the midportion (body). The epididymal duct measures several meters in length when fully expanded. The distal portion (tail) of the epididymis extends almost to the lower pole of the testis and has a less convoluted course. It emerges into the ductus deferens. The transport of sperm through the epidymis is a result of peristaltic action of contractile cells in the walls and action by ciliated cells lining the ductal lumen.

Embryological development

During gestation, differentiation of the gonads into testes becomes apparent at about the seventh week. The earliest evidence is the cords of cells, which extend at right angles to the longitudinal axis of the gonad. These cell cords become the seminiferous tubules that eventually join the portion of the wolffian duct which becomes the future ductus deferens (vas deferens). The seminiferous tubules are solid during most of their intrauterine life and are composed primarily of germ cells. Evidence of lumen formation becomes apparent near the end of gestation. In the early stages of gestational life, the seminiferous tubules are surrounded by large numbers of interstitial cells. As the fetus increases in size, the tubules occupy an increasing proportion of the total volume of the gonad and the interstitial cells become correspondingly reduced. The structure of the testes undergoes very few changes until after puberty.

The primitive gonad develops on the medial aspect of the mesonephric ridge. In the male embryo, the testes descend from their original location in the posterior portion of the midabdominal cavity during the early months of gestation. The testes do not begin their actual descent into the scrotum until about the seventh gestational month. At this time, they are drawn through the inguinal canal into the scrotum by fibrous bands known as the gubernaculum testis. This movement is intermittent, and from the late gestational period through the early perinatal period the testes may be found either in the inguinal canal or in the scrotum. As the testes become established in the scrotum, the inguinal canal closes and each testis is partially enveloped in a portion of peritoneal sac that has been carried down into the scrotum by the descending testis.

FUNCTIONAL UNITS OF SEMINIFEROUS TUBULES

The fundamental achitecture of the seminiferous epithelium is based on a central Sertoli cell and an arrangement of germ cells surrounding it.[4,5] Each Sertoli cell extends centripetally from the basement membrane of the seminiferous tubule to the center of the lumen. The most immature germ cells lie on the basement membrane while the spermatids and sperma-

tozoa are positioned toward the center of the tubule. The Sertoli cell unit represents a channel of communication from the vascular supply outside the basement membrane to all the developing germ cells surrounding it. Transport of nutrients takes place centripetally through the Sertoli cell. The spermatogonia and spermatocytes lie in juxtaposition to the plasma membrane of the Sertoli cell. Large portions of the spermatids are embedded in the cytoplasm of the cell. Cyclical changes occur in the Sertoli cell in conjunction with the maturation and development of the surrounding germ cells. The Sertoli cell nucleus tends to rise as the immature spermatozoa ascend toward the lumen. The cell remains anchored to the basement membrane, and delicate intracytoplasmic linear fibrils are oriented longitudinally to this membrane. Prior to the release of spermatozoa, there is an elongation of the cytoplasm and nucleus, with a decrease in the fat and carbohydrate content. As the spermatozoa are released into the lumen, the Sertoli nucleus returns to the basal portion of the cell and the cycle begins again with the next spermatic generation.

SPERMATOGENESIS

Spermatogenesis is the process by which the male gamete is produced. This process does not occur simultaneously in all parts of the testis or even in all portions of the same tubule. Activity within the seminiferous epithelium is cyclical,[6] and in man, areas of active seminiferous epithelium are interspersed among resting epithelia. Reconstructions from serial sections of the tubule have shown that areas of activity vary markedly in size and contour.[7] Cell associations occupy many small areas along the wall of the tubule, and atypical cellular associations are produced where the cells of adjacent territories mix.

In man and other mammals, the spermatogonia, spermatocytes, and spermatids are grouped in well-defined cellular associa-

45

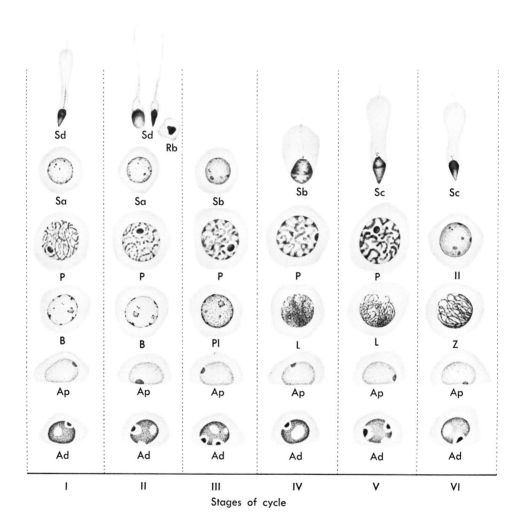

Fig. 4-2. Composition of six typical cellular associations observed in seminiferous epithelium of man. Each column consists of various cell types constituting such a cell association, which follow one another in any given area of seminiferous tubule according to sequence indicated from left to right. Transformation of type B spermatogonia into spermatozoa can be followed by reading along row from *B* and going successively to row above. Cellular associations, identified by Roman numeral, give "stage of cycle." *Ad*, Dark type A spermatogonia; *Ap*, pale type A spermatogonia; *B*, type B spermatogonia; *Pl*, preleptotene primary spermatocyte; *L*, leptotene primary spermatocyte; *Z*, zygotene primary spermatocyte; *P*, pachytene primary spermatocyte; *II*, secondary spermatocytes; *Sa* to *Sd*, consecutive steps of spermiogenesis; *Rb*, residual cytoplasmic body. (From Clermont, Y.: Fertil. Steril. **17**:705, 1966.)

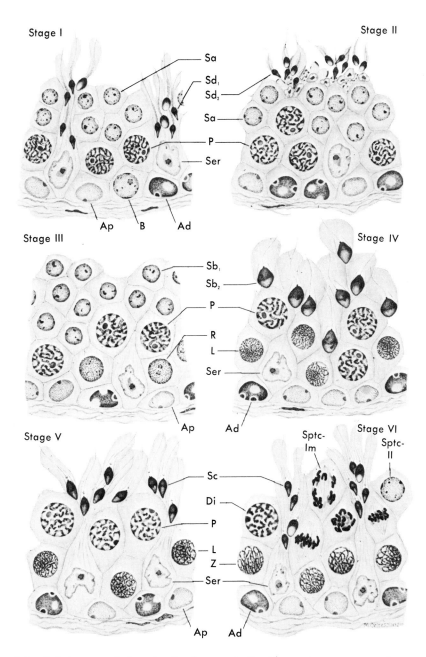

Fig. 4-3. Cellular associations in the human testis. These stages represent one cycle of the germinal epithelium. *Ser,* Sertoli cell; *Ad* and *Ap,* dark and pale type A spermatogonia; *B,* type B spermatogonia; *R,* resting or preleptotene spermatocytes; *L,* leptotene spermatocytes; *Z,* zygotene spermatocytes; *P,* pachytene spermatocytes; *Im,* primary spermatocytes in division; *II,* secondary spermatocytes; *Sa, Sb, Sc, Sd,* spermatids in various steps of spermiogenesis. (From Clermont, Y.: Amer. J. Anat. **112:**35, 1963.)

tions (Fig. 4-2).[8],[9] The youngest generation (spermatogonium) is situated closest to the basement membrane of the tubule, while the more mature cell type (spermatozoon) is closer to the center of the lumen. The cell associations are of fixed composition; one or two generations of spermatids are always associated with spermatocytes and spermatogonia at the same step of their respective development. Six well-defined cellular associations are identified in the human (Fig. 4-3). The cycle found in seminiferous epithelium is the sequence of events in which the six cellular associations advance consecutively to completion in a given area of seminiferous epithelium.

Spermatogonia

The walls of the seminiferous tubules are lined with spermatogonia and Sertoli cells. Spermatogonia are large cells with prominent nuclei having a paucity of organelles in the cytoplasm; they are the least differentiated cells of the germ cell population.

Several types of spermatogonia exist (Fig. 4-4). The most primitive elements are termed spermatogonia, type A, dark, because in sections of seminiferous tubules, the cytoplasm of these cells stains darkly with the periodic acid–Schiff (PAS) stain. The cell lacks nucleoli and the cytoplasm contains few organelles, as is usually the case with highly undifferentiated cells. A rare Golgi body and a few scattered mitochondria make up the entire organelle population of the cell. Spermatogonia are the only cells of the germ cell population that divide by mitosis; mitosis of the dark type A serves not only to give rise to more differentiated germ cells; this process also renews the population of the dark type A spermatogonia (Fig. 4-5). If mitosis produced only the more highly differentiated cells, the seminiferous tubules would soon be depleted of stem cells. In this process, as the dark type A spermatogonia divide mitotically, approximately 50% of the resultant cell population is of the same primitive

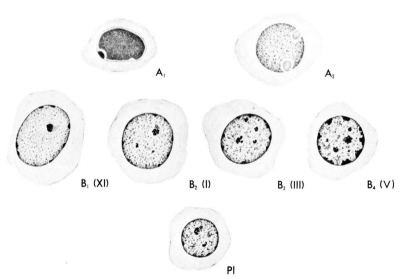

Fig. 4-4. Series of drawings illustrating the various types of spermatogonia as seen in dissecting tubules stained with hematoxylin and mounted "in toto." Types A_1 and A_2 spermatogonia were seen in all stages of the cycle. The various type B spermatogonia were found at the stages of the cycle indicated by the numbers in parentheses. Preleptotene spermatocytes (Pl) were seen in stages VI, VII, and VIII of the cycle. (From Clermont, Y.: Amer. J. Anat. **126:**57, 1969.)

stem cell type and the remaining 50% develops into the light type A spermatogonium.

Spermatogonia, type A, pale, are distinguished by the increased number of organelles in the cytoplasm and the presence of prominent nucleoli in the nucleus. In PAS-stained sections, the cytoplasm of the spermatogonia, light type A, cells stains lightly in contrast to the less differentiated dark-staining spermatogonia. Each pale type A cell divides to yield more highly differentiated spermatogonia, type B. These spermatogonia are classified on the basis of the nuclear characteristics, which in these cells show large nuclei in comparison to the amount of cytoplasm. Each nucleus contains a nucleolus with scattered chromatin granules. The type B spermatogonium in turn divides mitotically to produce resting

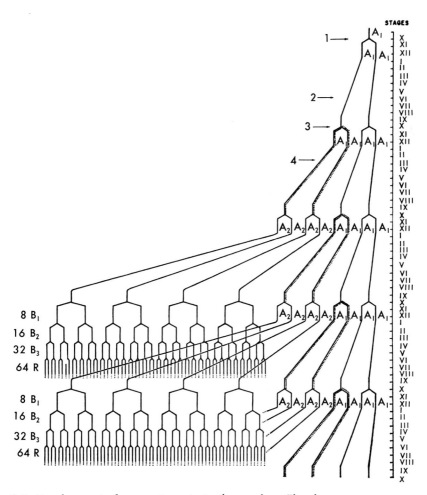

Fig. 4-5. Development of spermatogonia in the monkey. The diagram encompasses five consecutive cycles of the seminiferous epithelium, the stages of which are indicated by Roman numerals on the right-hand side. A_1 and A_2 are type A_1 and A_2 spermatogonia; B_1, B_2, and B_3, types B_1, B_2, and B_3 spermatogonia; R, resting primary spermatocytes. The two cycles at the base of the diagram show the behavior of all spermatogonial types. Arrows 1 to 4 show four possible sites for the initiation of differentiation. (From Clermont, Y., and Leblond, C. P.: Amer. J. Anat. 104:237, 1959.)

spermatocytes. In man, new stem cells arise from the first spermatogonial division and new spermatocytes arise from the third spermatogonial division.

Little is known about the initial impetus for differentiation of primitive sperm cell development into primary spermatocytes. It has been suggested that an inducer sub-

stance(s) may be present in the environment and direct the type A spermatogonia toward differentiation. It has been hypothesized that an unequal distribution of either the controlling cytoplasmic units or the chromosomal material may give rise to a differentiation-inducing material for one of the two type A, dark, cells. Furthermore

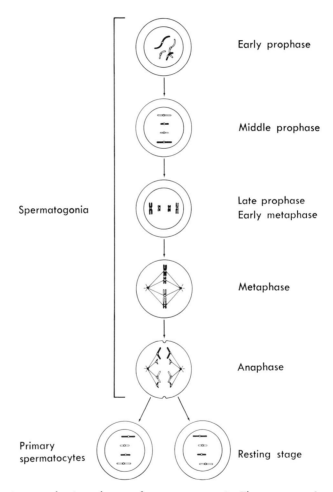

Fig. 4-6. Mitotic reproduction phases of spermatogenesis. The process of cell division is divided into three stages: (1) prophase, (2) metaphase, and (3) anaphase. During prophase, the chromosomes first become visible and begin their migration. Prophase may be subdivided into four additional stages (leptotene, zygotene, pachytene, and diplotene). During metaphase, they are lined in an organized fashion, grouped for distribution to daughter cells. During anaphase, the chromosomes and surrounding cytoplasm have separated and the daughter cells are forming. After cell division ceases, an interphase, or resting stage, commences in which the chromosomes are dispersed throughout the nucleus.

at certain critical periods of the cycle, the spermatogonia are vulnerable to degeneration, thereby suggesting the origination of the cell-degenerating factor at these times.

Spermatocytes

Type B spermatogonia divide by mitosis to give rise to a new generation of cells, the primary spermatocytes (Fig. 4-6). At first these cells enter a resting stage, termed an interphase, in preparation for the division of the cell chromosomes by meiosis. The interphase nuclei of primary spermatocytes resemble the nuclei of their precursors, the type B spermatogonia. Both contain dark- and pale-staining chromatin granules, although the chromatin is more deeply stained in the majority of nuclei in the spermatocyte. The nucleolus, centrally located, is covered with a dense, chromophilic chromatin. Immediately prior to the meiotic prophase at the end of interphase, the amount of deoxyribonucleic acid (DNA) is doubled. This is the final synthesis of DNA in spermatogenesis. This prophase of the first maturation division is of long duration, and during this period the chromosomes vary in form, ranging from a filamentous, beaded configuration to a shortened and thickened shape.

Intercellular bridges provide an open communication between spermatocytes.[10] These intercellular bridges are found in man as well as in many other species. The bridges are relatively short and are surrounded by a thickening of the plasma membrane at the junction of the two cells. Mitochondria and other organelles pass from one cell to another through these communications. The bridges are maintained through both the secondary spermatocyte series and the stage of spermatid development. Spermatid clusters usually consist of 8 conjoined cells with intercellular bridges. A thin cytoplasmic filament of the contiguous Sertoli cell extends into the cleft between the two conjoined cells. It is likely that the Sertoli cell cytoplasm is active in maintaining the communication between cells. Intercellular bridges cannot account for the simultaneous development of spermatocytes and spermatid, for it has been observed that hundreds of cells may undergo simultaneous development. It is possible that the presence of intercellular bridges represents a controlling factor so that an average of 8 (range 6 to 13) spermatids may be attached to any one Sertoli cell.

Following the meiotic prophase, the primary spermatocytes undergo the first maturation division giving rise to secondary spermatocytes (Fig. 4-7). During this process, the chromosomal content of each primary spermatocyte is reduced from the diploid (46) to the haploid (23) number, the genetic material is redistributed, and the X and Y chromosomes are segregated. The interphase nucleus of the secondary spermatocyte is much smaller than that of the primary spermatocyte just before meiosis, and it contains deeply stained chromatin with several large chromophilic masses.

During the prolonged meiotic prophase, pairing of homologous chromosomes occurs prior to cell division. At first the 46 chromosomes appear as slender single threads (leptotene stage of prophase); following this, the homologous chromosomes lie parallel to each other with the formation of 23 bivalent components (zygotene stage). In the next stage (pachytene), each chromosome splits longitudinally as in mitosis, but remains joined at the centromere to form a tetrad of 4 chromatids. The centromere is a thickened point of attachment of the spindle fibers to the chromatid pairs; it is at this point that the chromatids may break away, forming a tetrad of 4 chromatids. During the diplotene stage, as the homologous strands separate, they are pulled by the spindle fibers that are attached to more peripheral asters, and they subsequently form the metaphase plate. The 2 chromatids and the centromere making up each chromosome become oriented

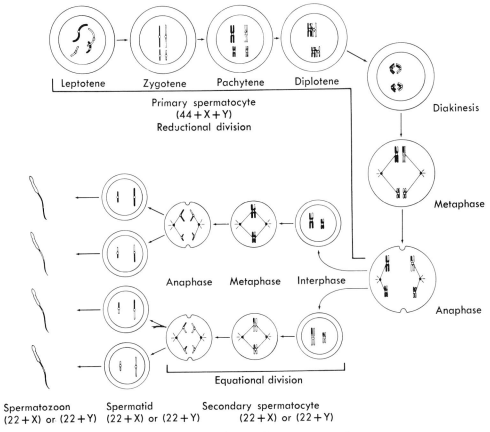

Leptotene   Zygotene   Pachytene   Diplotene

Primary spermatocyte
(44 + X + Y)
Reductional division

Diakinesis

Metaphase

Anaphase

Anaphase   Metaphase   Interphase

Equational division

Spermatozoon   Spermatid   Secondary spermatocyte
(22 + X) or (22 + Y)   (22 + X) or (22 + Y)   (22 + X) or (22 + Y)

Fig. 4-7. Meiotic phases of spermatogenesis.

on the spindle. When the cell divides, each chromatid pair moves toward the opposite poles. Each chromosome is still double-stranded except at the centromere; however, they are no longer genetically identical to the parent cell. Each secondary spermatocyte receives 22 autosomes and either an X or a Y chromosome. Between the transformation from the primary spermatocyte to the metaphase of the secondary spermatocyte, an interphase occurs, which is relatively short as compared to the long prophase of the first maturation division. The interphase nucleus of the secondary spermatocyte is much smaller than the late pachytene spermatocyte nucleus. It resembles the nucleus of a young spermatid and is readily identified by its larger size. As the secondary spermatocyte proceeds through

the second maturation division to yield spermatids, the diad splits at the centromere to form 2 monads. One monad, after having undergone a typical meiotic longitudinal replication, passes to each spermatid. Intercellular bridges connect the secondary spermatocytes and usually a syncytial clone (mass of cytoplasm with numerous nuclei) has an average of 8 nuclei in each cluster.

SPERMIOGENESIS
Spermatids

The process of spermiogenesis begins with the spermatid stage (Figs. 4-8 and 4-9). This phase is characterized by continuous maturation of both nucleus and cytoplasm of the spermatid, eventually leading to differentiation into a young spermatozoon. Neither mitosis nor meiosis oc-

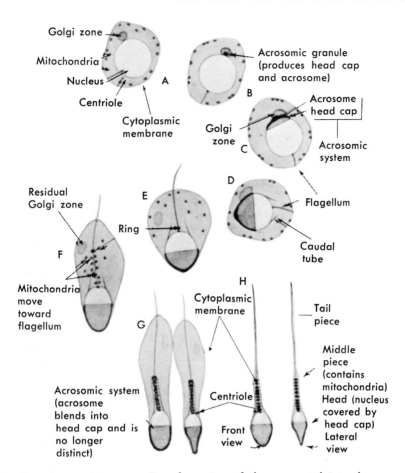

Golgi zone

Mitochondria

Nucleus

Centriole

Cytoplasmic membrane

A

Acrosomic granule (produces head cap and acrosome)

B

Golgi zone

Acrosome head cap

Acrosomic system

C

D

Residual Golgi zone

Ring

Mitochondria move toward flagellum

E

F

Flagellum

Caudal tube

H

G

Acrosomic system (acrosome blends into head cap and is no longer distinct)

Cytoplasmic membrane

Centriole

Front view

Tail piece

Middle piece (contains mitochondria)

Head (nucleus covered by head cap)

Lateral view

Fig. 4-8. Spermiogenesis in man. Transformation of the spermatid into the spermatozoon. (After Clermont, Y., and Leblond, C. P.: Amer. J. Anat. **96**:229, 1955; from Ham, A. W.: Histology, ed. 6, Philadelphia, 1969, J. B. Lippincott Co.)

curs at this stage. It is during this stage that the spermatid is engulfed in the cytoplasm of the Sertoli cell. Formation of a thin layer covering about two thirds of the sperm head (the acrosome) is noted early in the process of spermiogenesis. In the spermatid, the Golgi complex consists of a system of closely packed tubules and vesicles localized close to the nucleus. Shortly after the second maturation division occurs, the Golgi apparatus of the spermatid tends to orient itself on one side of the nucleus and to show signs of increased activity. Numerous small vesicular elements are produced by the Golgi apparatus and appear

as dense bodies that are known as the proacrosomic granules. These granules coalesce and form the acrosome, which contains mucopolysaccharides and has acid phosphatase and nucleoside phosphatase activity. Simultaneously the nuclear material begins to condense into coarse granules, and as the configuration of the sperm head approaches its definitive shape, the nucleoplasm is filled with tightly packed dense granules. As these morphological changes take place, the composition of the nuclear proteins undergoes significant alterations. Basic proteins such as histones and protamines combine with the DNA and in this

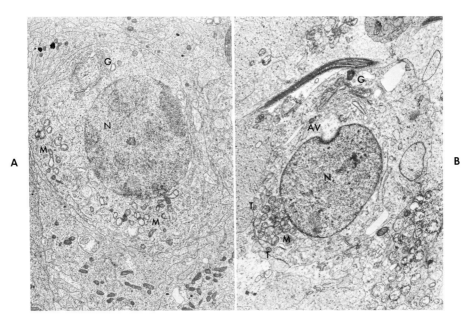

Fig. 4-9. Electron micrographs of maturing spermatids (monkey) during spermiogenesis. **A,** Early spermatid showing a centrally located nucleus with orientation of the Golgi apparatus toward one pole and diffuse distribution of mitochondria in the cytoplasm. **B,** Spermatid showing development of the acrosomal vesicle in juxtaposition to the Golgi apparatus. Orientation of mitochondria at the pole opposite to the Golgi apparatus is indicated, as well as formation of the rudimentary tail in juxtaposition to the coalesced mitochondria. The axial filament complex represents the portion of tail that will develop into the middle piece. The vesicles in the cytoplasm are normal for this stage of development. **C,** A spermatid during the late stage of spermiogenesis shows condensation of the nuclear material as an electron-dense structure surrounded by a thin acrosome, which will surround and adhere to the distal portion of the sperm nucleus. The cytoplasmic material engulfing the nucleus and acrosome will eventually be abosrbed. Organization of the axial fibers in the middle piece shows most fibers to be in a longitudinal orientation and these fibers are surrounded by coalesced mitochondria that are oriented in a helical formation. Two cytoplasmic droplets, the smaller adjoining the base of the nucleus and the larger droplet containing vesicles and appearing in the lower right-hand corner of the photograph, will shortly be absorbed. *A,* Acrosome; *AV,* acrosomal vesicle; *C,* cytoplasmic droplet; *G,* Golgi apparatus; *M,* mitochondria; *MP,* middle piece; *N,* nucleus; *T,* rudimentary tail.

manner bind the chromatin into a three-dimensional semicrystalline structure. In addition, these basic proteins neutralize the phosphoric acid groups of the nucleic acid. During spermiogenesis, the histones are replaced by protamines in some species (fish), and RNA and nonhistone proteins are lost during the metamorphosis.

Development of the flagellum takes place on the sperm head opposite the acrosomal development. This change involves the two centrioles of the spermatid and the formation of new structures in the cytoplasm on the posterior surface of the nucleus. The proximal centriole elongates by adding several centriolar segments,

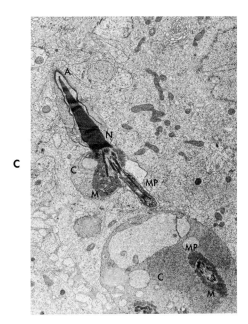

Fig. 4-9, contd. For legend see opposite page.

separated from one another by translucent lines that represent successive stages of centriolar growth. The distal centriole forms the connecting piece as it is transformed into a circular system of segmented columns surrounding the proximal region of the flagellum. At their distal ends, these columns are continuous with the outer dense fibers of the flagellum. At their proximal ends, they connect with the markedly enlarged proximal centriole. The elements of the axial filament complex of the flagellum are directly continuous with the triads of the proximal centriole. It is likely that the proximal centriole acts as the kinetic center of the sperm flagellum. A ringlike structure surrounds each flagellum where it protrudes from the main body of the cell; it is believed that this annulus is responsible for the synthesis of the contractile proteins that comprise the outer dense fibers of the axial filaments. Mitochondria aggregate and form a sheath around the axial filament behind the sperm head and are eventually arranged in a spiral fashion, forming a mitochondrial helix in the middle piece of the spermatozoa. Much of the cell cytoplasm migrates to an area around the middle piece, forms a residual body, and is eventually pinched off and cast away. A tightly fitting plasma membrane now covers the spermatozoon, except at the junction of the nucleus and flagellum where a small bead of cytoplasm is usually retained.

The mature spermatozoon

The mature sperm of each mammalian species has a distinctive appearance (Fig. 4-10).[11] The human spermatozoon may be characterized as having a head and a tail. The head consists of the nucleus and acrosome; the tail consists of the neck, middle piece, principal piece, and endpiece. The ovoid head is flattened anteriorly and appears pearlike in profile. The nucleus consists of a densely staining chromatin material in which small vacuoles may be seen. Covering most of the anterior nucleus is the acrosomal cap, together with both the inner and outer acrosomal membranes. Over the posterior half of the nucleus is a nuclear membrane. The plasma membrane of the head is continuous with the other parts of the sperm. Vacuoles noted within the nucleus are variable in size and may be found in different locations although they are more prominent in the anterior half.

The axial filaments arise from the centrioles in the neck of the spermatozoon and consist of a central pair of fibrils surrounded by two concentric rings of 9 fibrils each. The outer dense fibers assume a smaller diameter in the principal piece, and each of the 9 fibrils terminates at somewhat different levels. As they approach their termination, the outer fibers become fanlike with the apex pointing toward the corresponding doublet of the axial filament complex. Each outer fiber fuses with the corresponding doublet of the axial complex. It is likely that the outer fibers are the contractile elements of the spermatozoon. The central fibers and inner ring are continued throughout the tail, giving the nine plus two (9 + 2) arrangement char-

55

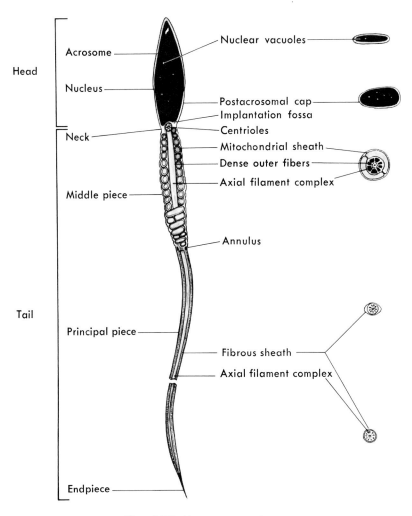

Fig. 4-10. Mature spermatozoon.

acteristic of motile cilia observed in mammals. Surrounding the axial filament in the middle piece of the spermatozoon is a group of mitochondria arranged in a spiral fashion. The mitochondria are single structures that do not coalesce but form a continuous mitochondrial helix throughout the middle piece. The mitochrondrial helices are responsible for the liberation and transfer of energy to the axial fibers, which in turn produce locomotion of the spermatozoa.

The fibrous sheath envelops the principal piece of the tail and consists of a large number of riblike structures. The ribs are composed of a dense fibrillar material that fuses at both extremities with two longitudinal columns on each transverse plane representing attachment structures. Close to the end of the principal piece, both the transverse and the longitudinal elements of the fibrous sheath are reduced in thickness prior to their termination. The site of termination represents transition from the principal piece to the endpiece. Overlying the entire head and tail is a plasma membrane that is continuous throughout the entire spermatozoon.

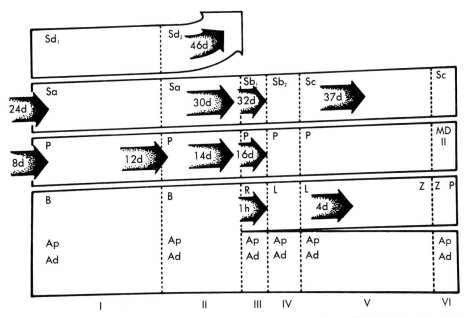

Fig. 4-11. Diagram illustrating the position of the most advanced labeled cells within the cycle of the seminiferous epithelium at various time intervals after an intratesticular injection of thymidine-³H. Framework of the diagram gives the cellular composition of the six stages of the cycle, space allotted to the stages being proportional to their relative durations. Arrows correspond to the most advanced labeled cells at the various time intervals after injection, indicated on the arrows themselves. Ad, Ap, B, R, L, Z, P, respectively, resting leptotene, zygotene, pachytene, primary spermatocytes; MD, maturation divisions; II, secondary spermatocytes; Sa, Sb_1, Sb_2, Sc, Sd_1, Sd_2, steps of spermiogenesis. At one hour after thymidine-³H injection, the resting spermatocytes are the most advanced labeled cells; 46 days later, the Sd_2 spermatids become labeled and are the most advanced cells. Between these two time intervals, various other elements constitute the group of the most advanced labeled cells. (From Heller, C. G., and Clermont, Y.: Recent Progr. Hormone Res. **20**:545, 1964; copyrighted by Academic Press, Inc.)

DURATION OF THE SPERMATOGENIC CYCLE

In the human, the duration of one cycle is 16 ± 1 days (Fig. 4-11).[7] The total length of spermatogenesis involves several cycles, and the total number of days depends upon the location of the starting point. When the first stem cell totally committed to cell division (spermatogonium, type A, light) is established as the starting point, the length of spermatogenesis is 4.5 cycles or 74 ± 5 days. Less commonly, the earliest primitive stem cell (spermatogonium, type A, dark) may be the starting point; in these cells, however, only about 50% will produce the more differentiated cell type (type A, light), while the remainder continue to produce new stem cells (type A, dark). Using type A, light, spermatogonia as the starting point, the total duration of spermatogenesis is 90 days, or about one cycle longer. In both calculations, the end point of spermatogenesis is always considered to be the time when spermatozoa are released by the Sertoli cell and are lying free in the lumen.

SPERM TRANSPORT AND THE MALE ACCESSORY GLANDS

The epididymis

Following completion of the process of spermiogenesis, the sperm in the lumina of the seminiferous tubules are advanced along these tubules. The sperm first enter the efferent ductules and proceed into the tortuous ducts of the epididymis; the tail of the epididymis is the principal reservoir for spermatozoa. The walls of the epididymis are lined with secretory epithelium, which appears as columnar cells having nonmotile stereocilia. In addition to the nutritional functions of the fluid secreted by these cells, a process of maturation of the sperm takes place while they occupy the confines of the epididymis. Sperm are capable of surviving longer in the epididymis than in any other portion of the male reproductive tract. The spermatozoa are immotile in the epididymis and develop motility only when they come in contact with oxygen or a substance capable of being metabolized to lactic acid.

The epididymal secretion is characterized by a relatively high content of potassium in comparison with the whole semen content.[12] In several other mammals, the amount of potassium in the epididymal secretions is either equal to or double that of sodium, while the amount of sodium is usually two to three times that of the potassium content in the seminal plasma. High concentrations of glycerylphosphorylcholine are also present in the epididymal secretions.[13] The total amount varies according to the species; in the boar, for example, the amount of glycerylphosphorylcholine may be as high as 3% of the total concentration. Glycerylphosphorylcholine is a potential energy source for spermatozoa. Unlike fructose, which may be metabolized directly by the spermatozoa, the utilization of glycerylphosphorylcholine for energy is dependent upon an enzyme that splits choline from the glycerylphosphorylcholine molecule, thus liberating glycerophosphate, which in turn may be directly metabolized by the spermatozoa. This enzyme, glycerophosphorocholine diesterase, has been found in the uterine secretions of the ewe, cow, sow, and rat and is an endometrial product rather than one of bacterial origin. Following the splitting of choline, the glycerophosphate enters the glycolytic cycle with liberation of energy and a concomitant breakdown to lactic acid and finally to water and carbon dioxide. Numerous enzymes, including glycosidases such as α-mannosidase and β-N-acetylglucosaminidase, have been detected in epididymal secretions. Both occur in high concentrations and are very active in the metabolism of the corresponding sugar. Both mannose and N-acetylglucosamine are known to be present in the acrosomes of ejaculated spermatozoa, and it is possible that some intracellular components of spermatozoa may be acquired during their residence in the epididymis. Cytolysis of the phagocytes found in the epididymis, as well as degradation of nonejaculated spermatozoa, takes place in this region and may contribute some components to the fluid.

The ductus deferens (vas deferens)

The tail of the epididymis is less convoluted and gives rise to a long curved duct (the ductus deferens) (Fig. 4-12). This duct ascends along the posterior border of the testis and becomes a constituent of the spermatic cord, traversing the inguinal canal, eventually crossing the dome of the bladder and entering the prostatic urethra. Prior to its entry into the prostate gland, the ductus deferens is joined by the main excretory duct of the seminal vesicle, and both form the ejaculatory duct, which traverses through the prostate. Immediately before its entry into the prostate, the ductus becomes enlarged and tortuous and is then called the terminal ampulla. Within the ampulla is a folded epithelial membrane that forms an intricate system of spaces and functions as a secondary storehouse for

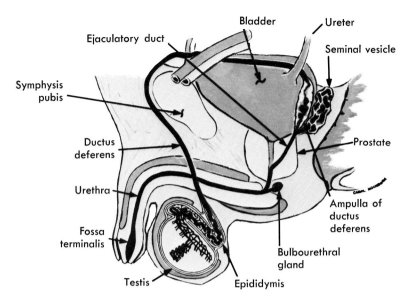

Fig. 4-12. Male reproductive system.

spermatozoa. Although stereocilia are present in the proximal part of the ductus deferens, they are absent from the distal part, including the ampulla. The ampulla serves to store the accumulated tubule secretions moistening the sperm. The secretions from the ampulla are yellow in color and contain a high content of ergothioneine.[14] This substance has the ability to reduce chemical compounds and is a major component of semen in other animals (e.g., the stallion). It is only occasionally present in small amounts in the human. Small amounts of fructose are also found in the secretions of the ampulla. In contrast to other species studied, the stallion has a relatively large ampulla, which at times may exceed the other accessory glands in size.

The seminal vesicles

The seminal vesicles are two lobulated glands situated between the bladder and the rectum. Columnar secretory epithelium lines the diverticula of the seminal vesicles. These glands secrete a fluid that becomes integrated with the sperm mass during ejaculation. The resulting secretion is a viscid fluid, rich in substances such as fructose, phosphorylcholine, and proteins such as globulins.

The storage capacity of the seminal vesicles in the human is small, when compared to other animals such as the bull or the boar; in the cat and dog, however, there are no seminal vesicles. The secretions of the seminal vesicles in the human have an unusually high content of reducing substances, and both citric acid and fructose are present in high amounts (125 mg and 315 mg/100 ml, respectively). Ascorbic acid, inorganic phosphorus, and acid-soluble phosphorus are present in lesser amounts. Potassium is the major cation and is present in high concentrations, measuring 20 millimoles; there is a relative absence of sodium. Citric acid is the primary anion and chlorides are present in very low amounts. In incubation experiments, slices of seminal vesicle mucosa maintained their potassium content both aerobically and anaerobically.[15] Cellular toxins such as iodoacetate caused a loss of potassium and a corresponding increase in sodium. Adenosine triphosphate is required for the retention of potassium and if this energy source is depleted, the potassium is replaced by sodium. In most species studied, including man, the majority of fructose secreted is from the seminal vesicles. Additionally, in man, a small amount of fructose may be secreted from the ampulla, but not from the prostate gland. These high concentrations of fructose furnish energy for the spermatozoa after ejaculation occurs. There is no evidence that human spermatozoa are able to oxidize fructose directly by the phosphopentose pathway; it is probable that lactic acid provides the necessary energy. The fructose is metabolized by the mitochondrial enzymes of the middle piece with consequent liberation of the energy necessary for motility.

The prostate

The human prostate gland measures approximately 4 cm in diameter and lies in juxtaposition to the neck of the urinary bladder. The gland, which surrounds the urethra and the two ejaculatory ducts, is composed primarily of two prominent lateral lobes together with smaller anterior, posterior, and medial lobes. The two ejaculatory ducts are located between the middle and lateral lobes of the prostate. As they converge, they diminish in size and terminate in the prostatic urethra in close approximation to each other. The ejaculatory ducts are lined with secretory columnar epithelium and have numerous glandular evaginations that project into the substance of the prostate. The prostatic secretion is alkaline and its chief constituents are acid phosphatase, fibrinolysin, and calcium. During the ejaculatory process, the sperm traverse the ejaculatory ducts through the prostate, emerging into the prostatic portion of the urethra and continuing to the membranous and penile urethra. In man, the colorless prostatic secretion is slightly acidic with a pH of 6.5. Several strong proteolytic enzymes are present. High quantities of fibrinolysin are present; it is thus

possible to liquefy 50 ml of clotted human blood by 1 ml of prostatic fluid in about 18 hours. In man, the enzymes diastase and β-glucuronidase are found in the secretions and are relatively active. Usually less than 1% of the prostatic secretion is protein. The relative increase of free amino acids in prostatic secretion as compared to plasma is probably due to the action of proteolytic and transaminating enzymes in the prostatic tissue. Citric acid and acid phosphatase are secreted by the prostate gland. The presence of these two substances and the lack of fructose provide a convenient chemical indicator in differentiating the contributions to seminal plasma by the prostate gland from the seminal vesicular secretions. In humans, citric acid ranges from 480 to 2688 mg/100 ml and acid phosphatase content may be as high as 3950 King-Armstrong units/ml in the prostatic secretions.[16,17] In humans, osmotically active substances in prostatic fluids differ from those of the seminal vesicular fluid. For example, sodium is the main cation in prostatic fluid, having a value of 156 meq/L with potassium and calcium being relatively equal at 30 meq/L each. Citric acid is the major anionic constituent, and chlorides, bicarbonates, and phosphates comprise a minor portion of the anion concentration. Characteristic of the prostate gland is the high concentration of zinc. Injections of radioactive zinc into the bloodstream show a relatively large uptake in the prostate after 10 days. Depletion of zinc in the body following an intravenous injection of diphenylthiocarbazone results in severe damage to the glandular epithelium of the prostate.

Bulbourethral (Cowper's) and urethral (Littre's) glands

In humans, these glands are small and are composed of numerous lobes in close apposition to each other. The bulbourethral glands, located in the posterior portion of the urethra, secrete an abundance of mucoproteins. It is this material that is ejaculated prior to spermatozoa. Numerous widely dispersed smaller glands are present throughout the entire length of the urethra.

EJACULATION

During development in the seminiferous tubules and storage in the epididymis and ampulla, the sperm are nonmotile because of accumulation of acid metabolites. At the time of emission and ejaculation, the secretions of the accessory glands are alkaline and tend to neutralize the acid metabolites. In addition, the alkaline secretions mixed with the sperm at the time of ejaculation also partially neutralize the acidity of the vaginal fluid.

The process of ejaculation, which is mediated through the central nervous system, is a reflex process and occurs in two stages. During the emission phase, contraction of the smooth muscle surrounding the epididymis delivers the semen (spermatozoa and secretory fluids) into the posterior portion of the membranous urethra. The ejaculation phase is characterized by a spasmodic contraction of the bulbocavernosus muscle of the urogenital diaphragm, expelling the seminal fluid into the urethra. The accessory glands, on the other hand, do not expel their fluids simultaneously during the emission phase. A small amount of preejaculatory fluid is first produced by the urethral and bulbourethral glands. These secretions are followed by emission of fluids, first from the prostate and then the seminal vesicles, then by sperm from the ampulla of the ductus deferens, and finally by the main bulk of spermatozoa from the tail of the epididymis. The ejaculated fluid consists of spermatozoa, and the fluid portion is termed the seminal plasma. The seminal plasma is a mixture of secretions from accessory glands and secretions from ducts of the male genital system. Secretory fluids are produced in the epididymis, ductus deferens (including the ampulla), seminal vesicles, prostate, bulbourethral glands, and urethral glands. In the human, seminal plasma makes up a large portion of the ejaculated fluid, resulting in relatively dilute semen when compared with that of lower animals. In general, the secretory epithelium of the male accessory glands is highly specialized and relies heavily on testosterone for its development and secretory activity. The secretions of these glands are unusual in that they contain certain biochemical substances (such as fructose, phosphorylcholine, glycerylphosphorylcholine, and citric acid), which rarely have elevated concentrations elsewhere in the body. The semen also contains derivatives of the secretory cells which appear as globules and granules. Exfoliated epithelial cells and cellular debris are usually present in semen and are thought to be derived primarily from the epididymis.

SIGNIFICANCE OF THE MALE ACCESSORY GLAND SECRETIONS

The seminal plasma acts as a diluent for the thick mass of spermatozoa present in the epididymis. In order to develop motility, the spermatozoa must be diluted with an optimal amount of fluid. Shortage of fluid results in nonmotile spermatozoa; excessive dilution, following a rapid burst of activity, similarly results in a lack of motility and degradation. In vivo experiments have shown that the results of dilution of spermatozoa are essentially the same in mammals and lower vertebrates, and in the rabbit result in a loss of fertility.[18] In order to obtain maximal motility of sperm, the diluting fluid must contain small quantities of potassium (0.005 M), magnesium (0.012 M) and potassium ions with the omission of calcium ions. In addition, the activity of the spermatozoa depends upon the oxygen tension, temperature, and pH of the medium. The presence of a sulfate in the surrounding medium may enhance motility by protecting the lipid capsule of the sperm from the action of sodium chloride and thereby preventing the swelling of spermatozoa. In the rabbit, spermatozoa have greater fertilizing capacity when placed in a relatively small volume of salt diluent than in a much larger volume of the same diluent.

In addition to such activation of spermatozoa by means of dilution, specific substances in the seminal plasma induce motility. The presence of fructose in the secretions of the seminal vesicles provides the primary nutrient for sperm fertility. The buffering capacity of proteins and amino acids prevents deterioration by alterations of the pH. It has been demonstrated in *in vivo* experiments that spermatozoa are very sensitive to pH changes in the medium. Inorganic ions in the semen, such as phosphate, are also important in stabilizing the pH of the seminal plasma.

Chemical substances that inhibit fertility may also be found in seminal plasma. Very little is known about such substances in man. However in some stallions, the seminal plasma contains a sulfhydryl compound that has an adverse effect on fertility. In these animals, if the sulfhydryl level is less than 10 μg/ml, fertilization occurs in only one half of the mares; however, if the level of sulfhydryl is greater than 23 μg/ml, conception does not occur in any of the animals. These sulfhydryl compounds may be largely, though not entirely, ergothioneine. It has been found that the terminal fraction or the end portion of seminal emission may contain less sulfhydryl compounds; thus if this fraction contains sufficient spermatozoa, it may be used by breeders in those stallions in which the sulfhydryl content is great.

Substances that have the capacity to stimulate smooth muscle are present in semen in extremely low quantities.[19] Prostaglandins, found in human seminal plasma, are able to stimulate contractions of strips of human uterus; the substances are also capable of eliciting, in addition to this smooth muscle activity, a rise in pressure on the blood vessels. Human semen,

when diluted 100 times, produces an increase in the spontaneous muscular contractions of the uterus. There is no evidence that physiological amounts of prostaglandins change the oxygen consumption or the metabolism of glucose of sperm, although in one clinical study, infertility and low motility of sperm were associated with a high content of prostaglandin in the semen.

REFERENCES

1. Liang, D. S.: Anatomical structure of the testicular tubule, Invest. Urol. 4:285, 1966.
2. Clermont, Y.: Contractile elements in the limiting membrane of the seminiferous tubules of the rat, Exper. Cell Res. 15:438, 1958.
3. Ross, M. H., and Long, I. R.: Contractile cells in human seminiferous tubules, Science 153:1271, 1966.
4. Elftman, H.: Sertoli cells and testis structure, Amer. J. Anat. 113:25, 1963.
5. Sapsford, C. S.: The development of the Sertoli cell of the rat and mouse: its existence as a mononucleate unit, J. Anat. 97:225, 1963.
6. Perey, B., Clermont, Y., and Leblond, C. P.: The wave of the seminiferous epithelium in the rat, Amer. J. Anat. 108:47, 1961.
7. Heller, C. G., and Clermont, Y.: Kinetics of the germinal epithelium in man, Recent Progr. Hormone Res. 20:545, 1964.
8. Clermont, Y.: The cycle of the seminiferous epithelium in man, Amer. J. Anat. 112:35, 1963.
9. Clermont, Y.: Spermatogenesis in man: a study of the spermatogonial population, Fertil. Steril. 17:705, 1966.
10. Fawcett, D. W., Ito, S., and Slautterback, D.: The occurrence of intercellular bridges in groups of cells exhibiting synchronous differentiation, J. Biophys. Biochem. Cytol. 5:453, 1959.
11. Fawcett, D. W.: The structure of the mammalian spermatozoon, Int. Rev. Cytol. 7:195, 1958.
12. Rothschild, L., and Barnes, H.: Osmotic pressure of bull semen diluents, Nature 173:636, 1954.
13. Dawson, R. M. C., Mann, T., and White, I. G.: Glycerylphosphorylcholine and phosphorylcholine in semen and their relation to choline, Biochem. J. 65:627, 1957.
14. Mann, T., Leone, E., and Polge, C.: The composition of the stallion's semen, J. Endocr. 13:279, 1956.
15. Whittam, R., and Breuer, H. J.: Ion transport

and metabolism in slices of guinea-pig seminal-vesicle mucosa, Biochem. J. **72**:638, 1959.

16. Huggins, C.: The prostatic secretion, Harvey Lect. **42**:148, 1948.

17. Gutman, A. B., and Gutman, E. B.: Quantitative relations of a prostatic component (acid phosphatase) of human seminal fluid, Endocrinology **28**:115, 1941.

18. Chang, M. C.: Effect of dilution of fertilizing capacity of rabbit spermatozoa, Science **104**:361, 1946.

19. Bergström, S., and Samuelsson, B.: Prostaglandins, Ann. Rev. Biochem. **34**:101, **1965**.

ADDITIONAL READINGS

Cross, B. A.: Hypothalamic influences on sperm transport in the male and female genital tract. In Lloyd, C. W.: Endocrinology of reproduction, New York, 1959, Academic Press, Inc.

Hartman, C. G.: Mechanisms concerned with conception, New York, 1963, The Macmillan Co.

Leblond, C. P., Steinberger, E., and Roosen-Runge, E. C.: Spermatogenesis. In Hartman, C. G.: Mechanisms concerned with conception, New York, 1963, The Macmillan Co.

Mann, T.: The biochemistry of semen and of the male reproductive tract, New York, 1964, John Wiley & Sons, Inc.

Wolstenholme, G. E. W., and O'Connor, M.: Endocrinology of the testis, Boston, 1967, Little, Brown & Co.

CHAPTER 5

Dynamic relationship of the ovary to the whole woman

In the preceding chapters the reader has been given a static view of the endocrine organs of reproduction. In the present chapter we shall attempt to integrate this and additional information into a picture of the dynamic aspects of female endocrine reproductive physiology. Fig. 5-1 is a schematic view of the processes involved. Fig. 5-2 is a diagrammatic presentation of the fluctuations in FSH, LH, progesterone, and estradiol observed during the normal menstrual cycle in women.

FLUCTUATIONS IN PITUITARY GONADOTROPINS AND GONADAL STEROIDS

FSH is slightly higher in the first half of the follicular phase of the menstrual cycle.[1] (The follicular phase is that portion preceding ovulation, during which follicle development is proceeding.) This FSH elevation *presumably* initiates the follicle development described in detail in Chapter 3. FSH then falls to low levels and is fairly constant until it peaks at midcycle, coincident with the LH peak. This LH-FSH peak causes discharge of the ovum from the now mature graafian follicle. FSH then falls to levels below those observed in the follicular phase and remains constant until menstruation. LH is low and increases gradually throughout the follicular phase, peaks sharply to cause ovulation, and then falls to levels below those seen in the follicular phase and remains fairly constant.[2,3] The LH-FSH ovulatory peak occurs between days 11 and 23 of the menstrual cycle,* and its timing appears to bear no relationship to the length of the cycle. LH peaks have been observed 8 to 17 days prior to the onset of menses.[3] After ovulation, LH and FSH fall to constant low levels.

Consideration of these fluctuations in LH and FSH together with the changes in blood concentrations of steroid hormones makes it evident that the two are not always directly related as cause and effect. Except for the early rise in FSH during the follicular phase, LH and FSH concentrations appear more or less constant and at slightly higher concentration than during the luteal phase. The changes in estradiol and progesterone depicted in Fig. 5-2 are summaries of a number of published studies on progesterone[4-8] and on estrogen.[9-12] Estradiol and possibly progesterone and 17-hydroxyprogesterone (not shown in Fig. 5-2) appear to be secreted in small amounts, and the amounts of estradiol and 17-hydroxyprogesterone increase prior to or concomitant with the LH-FSH midcycle peak.[9-12] Recall that during this period follicle growth and development are proceeding. Follicle growth and development, *once initiated*, appear to proceed to the preovulatory phase without any required *fluctua-*

---

*Day 1 is defined as the first day of menstrual flow; the last day of the cycle is defined as the day preceding the first day of next menstrual flow.

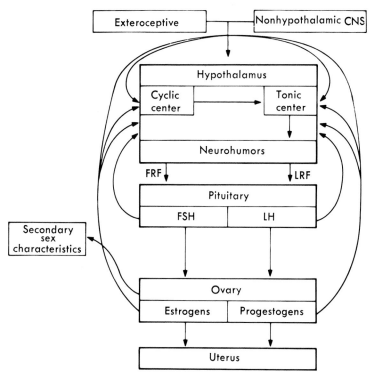

Fig. 5-1. Schematic presentation of the central nervous system–pituitary–ovarian inter-relations in women.

tions in LH and FSH. The slightly higher concentrations observed throughout the follicular phase, when compared to the luteal phase, may be required for follicle growth but data are inconclusive. Further support for the concept that FSH initiates follicle growth, which then proceeds independently, comes from the studies of Crooke et al.[13] Infertile patients were treated with a *single* injection of FSH. Ovulation was induced 6 or 7 days later by an injection of chorionic gonadotropin ("LH-like" hormone). After the FSH injection, FSH excretion increased, *then* returned to preinjection values, remaining there several days before ovulation was induced with chorionic gonadotropin. This indicated that follicle growth was continuing after the FSH had fallen to control levels. During the normal menstrual cycle, the LH-FSH ovulatory peak results in ovulation. A peak of 17-

hydroxyprogesterone and estradiol occurs prior to or coincident with the LH-FSH peak.* The possible significance of these changes is discussed later. After ovulation, the corpus luteum is formed and progesterone, estradiol, 17-hydroxyprogesterone, and other steroids are secreted in large amounts, while LH and FSH are low or undetectable. Alterations in blood concentrations of steroid hormones during the menstrual cycle are only presently being defined and there may be other physiologically important progestogens and estrogens not described herein.

For many years it was assumed that a periodic central nervous system cyclicity determined the timing of the ovulatory dis-

---

*17-Hydroxyprogesterone concentrations are not shown in Fig. 5-2. Data were available only in abstract form when this manuscript was prepared.

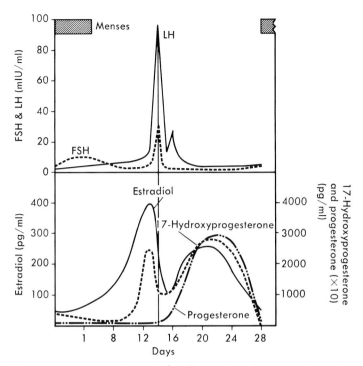

Fig. 5-2. Schematic representation of the fluctuations in serum luteinizing hormone (LH), follicle stimulating hormone (FSH), progesterone, 17-hydroxyprogesterone, and estradiol during the normal menstural cycle in women. Note that both estradiol and 17-hydroxyprogesterone rise before the LH-FSH ovulation surge. In order to show progesterone and 17-hydroxyprogesterone on the same scale, progesterone concentrations were divided by 10; that is, they are actually ten times greater than shown. (pg/ml = picograms per milliliter.)

charge of LH. However, consideration of the events occurring in the ovary indicates that some ovarian signal may relate to the LH-FSH peak so that the rise occurs when a ripened follicle is present. Odell and Swerdloff[14] have demonstrated that a typical "ovulatory" LH-FSH peak may be produced in castrate or postmenopausal women by sequential treatment with estrogen followed by estrogen plus a progestogen. Fig. 5-3 depicts such a study. They postulated that timing of the ovulatory peak resulted from an *ovarian signal* and that increasing progestogen levels might be that signal. Recent studies of estrogen concentrations[9-12] have revealed that estrogens increase prior to or coincident with the LH-

FSH peak. Thus it is possible that changes in estradiol, a progestogen, or both may trigger the ovulatory peak. The critical period just prior to the LH-FSH peak is presently the focus of extensive studies designed to clarify this point. Although administration of a progestogen to estrogen-suppressed castrate women has produced LH-FSH peaks, administration of estrogen alone for periods up to 60 days was not associated with peaks in LH or FSH. Administration of estrogen to normal women caused elevation and rather bizarre fluctuations in LH *without* increasing FSH.[15] These studies are discussed further in Chapter 12.

The data on progesterone concentrations

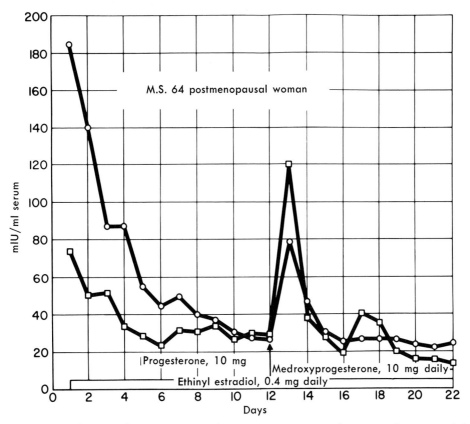

Fig. 5-3. Production of an LH-FSH peak in a postmenopausal woman, by sequential treatment with (1) estrogen and (2) estrogen plus a progestogen. Note that concentrations of FSH (o) are higher than LH (□) prior to estrogen treatment and that during the LH-FSH peak LH is higher than FSH. In spite of the continuation of progestogen treatment, the LH-FSH peak is of short duration. This patient received an injection of progesterone, which was then followed by oral medroxyprogesterone; but in other patients simulated ovulatory peaks have been produced in estrogen-suppressed postmenopausal women by using oral medroxyprogesterone only. The peaks are always produced within 12 to 24 hours of initiation of progestogen treatment. (From Odell, W. D., and Swerdloff, R. S.: Proc. Nat. Acad. Sci. **61**:529, 1968.)

are somewhat contradictory. Saxena et al.,[4] Runnebaum and Zander,[5] and perhaps Neill et al.[6] showed small elevations of progesterone prior to the LH peak. Yoshimi and Lipsett[7] failed to show a rise until after the LH peak, and Neill et al. apparently did not consider the small rise depicted in their studies as physiologically important. Strott et al.[8] have also shown that 17-hydroxyprogesterone increases before progesterone

does in women. The rise occurs prior to or coincident with the LH peak and might also be responsible for its induction. The follicular phase concentrations of progesterone are close to the limits of sensitivity of the assay systems used. Very recently, Abraham, Odell, and Swerdloff have developed radioimmunoassays for progesterone and 17-hydroxyprogesterone. Study of the menstrual cycle with these sensitive methods has revealed progesterone rises only after ovulation, but that in all instances 17-hydroxy-progesterone and estradiol always rise prior to or on the same day as the LH surge.

There is a considerable body of animal data suggesting that blood progesterone or progestogens may be important in preparing for the ovulatory surge of LH. In 1940 and 1943 Everett (see references listed in reference 14) showed that ovulation could be induced in rats with a spontaneously occuring state of persistent estrus by administration of progesterone. These animals had ovaries similar to those produced by androgen administration to newborn female rats (discussed later). Greer subsequently demonstrated that *destructive lesions* in the anterior hypothalamic region of rats could produce a similar constant estrus and ovulation could be induced by progesterone administration. Female monkeys become anovulatory during the summer, and Pfeiffer has shown that progesterone will induce ovulation during this period. (See references listed in reference 14.) Sawyer and Everett[16] have studied the effects of both estrogen and progesterone on ovulation in the rabbit, an animal that ovulates upon stimulation of the cervix during the estrus portion of the estrus cycle. Sequential estrogen treatment followed by progesterone treatment was required to permit ovulation upon cervical stimulation in nonestrus animals. Thus these important studies, if extended to the human, would indicate that preovulatory rises in both estrogen and progestogen may be important in initiating the ovulation surge in humans.

Once ovulation has occurred, the corpus luteum is formed. The blood concentrations of LH and FSH are lower during corpus luteum function than at any other portion of the cycle. However, Vande Wiele[17] has shown that small amounts of LH *are required* for normal corpus luteum function. When hypopituitary women were treated with human FSH (to induce follicle growth) and then induced to ovulate with human LH (rather than HCG), corpus luteum function could only be maintained normal by continued low-dose LH treatment. LH has a much shorter half time of disappearance than HCG, and earlier studies using HCG to induce ovulation had suggested that, once ovulation occurred, the corpus luteum functioned and ceased to function independent of pituitary secretion. However, it appears likely that the prolonged survival of HCG in blood maintained corpus luteum function after the single ovulating dose.

Prolactin is known to be required for normal corpus luteum function in the rat and mouse (see reference 4, Chapter 1). Treatment of rats with prolactin prolongs the life of the corpus luteum. However, in monkeys and in humans prolactin has failed to show any luteotropic actions. The functions of prolactin in the human, aside from its role in lactation, are not known. (See reference 2 for additional references.)

CENTRAL NERVOUS SYSTEM CONTROL

Whatever the signals are that initiate the ovulatory surge, they appear to act via the central nervous system. It is not appropriate in this text to discuss the entire wealth of data supporting the concept of central nervous control of gonadotropin secretion. Very little direct experimental data is available concerning central nervous control of LH and FSH secretion in women. Of necessity, we must therefore turn at this point to a discussion of animal experiments. There is no reason to believe at present that the general principles derived from these data do not apply to women. A portion of the anatomical data has been summarized in Chapter 2.

A number of workers reported between 1936 and 1948 that electrical stimulation of the hypothalamus of the rabbit (a reflex ovulator) could produce ovulation (summarized in references 18 and 19). Critchlow[18] reported in 1958 that in the rat (a spontaneous ovulator) stimulation of the ventral-medial hypothalamus resulted in ovulation. Everett[20] showed that hypophysectomy performed 40 to 60 minutes after stimulation did not interfere with ovulation, whereas hypophysectomy performed less than 40 minutes after stimulation prevented ovulation. The concept of a *hypophysiotropic area* of the hypothalamus has been forwarded by Halas et al. (see reference 21). Fig. 5-4 illustrates this area in the rat. (For references see reference 21.) Castration of an adult animal results in production of so-called pituitary castration cells; morphologically distinct changes are produced in the gonadotropin-secreting pituitary cells. If pituitary grafts were placed in castrated-hypophysectomized rats, these castration cells occurred only in the portions of the pi-

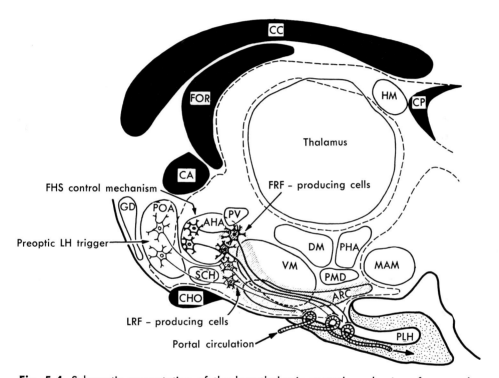

Fig. 5-4. Schematic presentation of the hypothalamic control mechanisms for gonadotropin secretion in the rat. The tonic center is located in the ventromedial-arcuate area, and the *FRF-* and *LRF*-producing neurons are indicated by the neural units with the dotted soma. They situate in the hypophysiotropic area (hatched) and their nerve endings terminate on the capillary loops of the portal system. The cyclic center is located in the preoptic region and its neurons are designated by the open soma. The axons from these cells extend to the tonic area. *AHA,* Anterior hypothalamic area; *ARC,* arcuate nucleus; *CA,* anterior commissure; *CC,* corpus callosum; *CHO,* optic chiasm; *CP,* posterior commissure; *FOR,* fornix; *DM,* dorsomedial nucleus; *GD,* gyrus diagonalis; *HM,* medial habenular nucleus; *MAM,* mammillary body; *PHA,* posterior hypothalamic area; *PLH,* posterior lobe hypophyses; *PMD, dorsal* premammillary nucleus; *POA,* preoptic area; *PV,* paraventricular nucleus; *SCH,* suprachiasmatic nucleus; *VM,* ventromedial nucleus. (Reproduced with permission from Flerko, B.: Brain mechanisms controlling gonadotrophin secretion and their sexual differentiation. In Lissak, K., editor: Symposium on reproduction, Budapest, 1967, Akadémiai Kiado.)

tuitary graft that were in direct contact with the crescent-shaped area in the hypothalamus (Fig. 5-4). This area is confined to a strip extending laterally about 1 mm on either side of the third ventricle and in a rostral-caudal direction immediately below the paraventricular nuclei to the mammillary region. In noncastrated rats, anterior pituitary grafts transplanted to this area show entirely normal cytology and maintain normal estrus cycles. Pituitary grafts placed under other areas of the central nervous system do not permit normal estrus cycles. Hypothalamic extracts, containing material from this area and other portions of the hypothalamus, contain luteinizing hormone releasing factor (LRF) and follicle-stimulating hormone releasing factor (FRF). (See Chapter 2.)

In the female, two central nervous areas appear to be involved in gonadotropin control mechanisms. A *"cyclic" area* is involved in the periodic ovulatory discharge. The anatomical location of this center in women has not been determined, but in female rats it is located in the anterior preoptic or suprachiasmatic area. A *"tonic" area* is also located in the hypothalamus of women and causes sufficient LH (? and FSH) discharge to maintain blood estrogen concentrations. This center also has not been anatomically identified in women but is located in the arcuate-ventromedial area in rats. (The arcuate nucleus does not appear in published studies of the human hypothalamus.) Much of the experimental evidence suggesting the existence of these areas has been published by Barraclough.[22] Barraclough and Gorski demonstrated that small doses of testosterone administered to female rats within a few days of birth would result in a nonfertile, noncycling animal at sexual maturity. No effect was seen in males. The ovaries of such androgen-sterilized females exhibited interstitial tissue hypertrophy with numerous large vesicular follicles, but no corpora lutea. Pituitary LH content was shown to be low, but

treatment with progesterone increased this content. When electrodes were placed in the ventromedial region of the hypothalamus from the preoptic area to below the ventromedial nuclei in androgen-sterilized, progesterone-treated rats, and an electrical stimulus was given, no ovulation resulted. (Recall that stimulation of this area in *normal female rats* invariably produces ovulation.) However, when androgen-sterilized, progesterone-treated rats received stimulation in the ventromedial-arcuate areas, ovulation occurred. Thus presumably androgen sterilization had affected the preoptic area, and the ventromedial-arcuate area was unaffected. Barraclough and Gorski thus proposed a theory of dual hypothalamic control of gonadotropin secretion (Fig. 5-1). According to this theory, the first level of hypothalamic control involves the *tonic* discharge of LH and FSH (via LRF and FRF) in sufficient amounts to maintain estrogen secretion. This area cannot initiate the ovulatory discharge of LH and FSH. This latter control center does not appear to be present in adult males. (This is discussed in Chapter 8.) All of these control mechanisms apply to the rat, mouse, and probably the rabbit. At present, the same basic structure is believed to apply to the human, but proof of this is not available.

There is also evidence that certain non-hypothalamic central nervous areas may modify gonadotropin secretion. Electrical stimulation of the amygdala led to ovulation in the rabbit, cat, and rat (see references 19 and 23). It also appears that the midbrain reticular formation is a participant in the ovulatory mechanism. Its role may not be clearly stated but it has been hypothesized[24] that (1) the reticular formation maintains the hypothalamus in an active state, while not being directly concerned with specific excitation, or (2) the specific excitation stimulus passes to the reticular activating system and then into the hypothalamus. Critchlow[25] has shown that bilateral lesions produced in the rostral midbrain area would prevent ovulation.

A variety of drugs that act on the central nervous system can be demonstrated to block ovulation in species in which the timing of ovulation is known (e.g., rabbit and rat). These include such drugs as reserpine, phenobarbital, morphine, atropine, and the phenothiazines. When administered chronically, the phenothiazines also produce a picture of persistent estrus with many follicles and no corpus luteum in rats—similar to that observed after hypothalamic lesions or androgen sterilization. In women, chronic administration of phenothiazines in high doses produces amenorrhea and persistent lactation. Barbiturates, atropine, morphine, and chlorpromazine (a phenothiazine) inhibit midbrain reticular formation and may prevent ovulation in this manner. Reserpine, on the other hand, does not decrease reticular formation activity and still inhibits ovulation. However, reserpine may inhibit input into the reticular activating system so that the brainstem is not repressed, but is inactive because of failure of input. Ovulation may be produced in reserpine-treated animals by direct hypothalamic stimulation.[24]

There is also evidence in the rat that a so-called short loop feedback may exist: that FSH may inhibit secretion of FSH, and LH inhibit secretion of LH.[26,27] The physiological significance of this mechanism is unknown for the rat, and its existence in the human has not been demonstrated.

As was indicated in Chapter 2, these hypothalamic control areas exert their influence by means of neural hormones secreted into the portal circulation and, in turn, reaching the anterior pituitary. Igarashi and McCann (see Chapter 2 for reference) made crude acidic extracts of adult rat hypothalamic tissue. Blood FSH was measured by the mouse uterine weight augmentation assay. These extracts when administered to castrate, estrogen-suppressed and progesterone-suppressed rats resulted in elevated blood FSH. No response was observed in hypophysectomized animals, indicating FSH per se was not being administered. This material was also demonstrated to be active in vivo and in vitro by the rat ovarian weight augmentation assay. McCann (references in Chapter 2) also reported that a luteinizing hormone–releasing factor existed. These factors are generally believed to be small polypeptides of molecular weight about 2000. Their amino acid sequence and composition remain unknown. Recall, however, that thyrotropin releasing factor (TRF) is a tripeptide (Glut-Hist-Prol).

PRODUCTION, DEGRADATION, AND EXCRETION OF FSH AND LH

The blood concentration of a hormone is determined by its volume of distribution, rate of degradation, and rate of secretion. In a steady state, the rate of secretion must equal the rate of degradation. When radioiodinated LH and FSH were injected as a single bolus intravenously, they showed a rapid multiexponential disappearance curve, never quite reaching a clearly linear slope. Fig. 5-5 illustrates the disappearance of these hormones from the blood of normal women. Note that LH disappears more rapidly than FSH. Because of the nonlinearity of these curves, a half time ($t\frac{1}{2}$) of disappearance could not be calculated from these studies. Integration of the entire area under the curve and calculation of metabolic clearance rates resulted in answers that were the same as those obtained by constant infusion techniques. The infusion method results in saturation of all compartments, and the area under the curve is automatically integrated. In such a case, labeled hormones were infused continuously into normal subjects until constant blood levels were obtained. At this point, the rate of infusion must equal degradation (and pituitary secretory rate in a steady state). Table 5-1 lists the secretory rates for both LH and FSH along with a com-

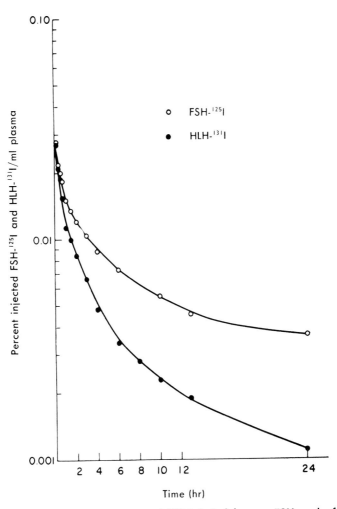

Fig. 5-5. Typical disappearance curves of ^{125}I-labeled human FSH and of ^{131}I-labeled LH after a single intravenous injection. The labeled hormones were simultaneously administered to this subject and were precipitated from plasma by the double antibody method. (From Coble, Y. D., Kohler, P. O., Cargille, C. M., and Ross, G. T.: J. Clin Invest. **48**:359, 1969.)

Table 5-1. Secretory and excretory rates for FSH and LH in women[*†]

Gonadal status	Hormone	Plasma LH (mIU/ml)	Metabolic clearance rate (ml/min)	Pituitary secretion rate (IU/day)	Urinary excretion rate (IU/day)	Approximate percent excreted
Premenopausal	LH	32.0 ± 9.6[‡]	24.4 ± 1.8	1056 ± 244	13-25	2
	FSH	10.0 ± 1.8	14.3 ± 1.1	210 ± 39	4.5-9	3
Postmenopausal	LH	99.2 ± 23.2	25.6 ± 4.1	3459 ± 587	131	4
	FSH	172 ± 24.0	12.6 ± 1.1	3083 ± 379	92.5	3

[*]Based on data from Kohler, Ross, and Odell, 1968, and Coble, Kohler, Cargille, and Ross, 1969.
[†]The fraction of both hormones that is excreted in the urine is less than 4%.
[‡]The LH values are high. These LH studies were performed in 4 women and one had an ovulatory LH peak at the time of study.

parison of *excretion* rates. The amount of FSH and LH excreted is only a small fraction of that produced each day. Renal clearance thus does not appear to be an important route of loss from the body. It is of interest that, although LH and FSH have some immunological and biochemical similarities, the degradative mechanisms clearly distinguish these two hormones. From other studies it is apparent that FSH and LH do not circulate bound to plasma proteins. The metabolic clearance rates (milliliters of plasma completely cleared of hormone each minute) for FSH and LH are similar for both normal women and postmenopausal women.[28,29] Thus the production rates (pituitary secretion) are accurately reflected by plasma concentrations, which may be used to indicate pituitary secretion. The metabolic clearance rates for FSH are less than for LH. Based upon published values for pituitary FSH and LH content, we estimate that the pituitary contains 50% to 100% of the FSH and LH secreted each day. The biochemistry and the sites of FSH and LH degradation remain unknown.

PRODUCTION AND DEGRADATION OF ESTRADIOL, PROGESTERONE, AND TESTOSTERONE

The pathways and cellular origins of ovarian steroid synthesis have been discussed in Chapter 2. As was stated earlier, probably the only physiologically important estrogen in women is estradiol. After secretion, this steroid is bound to a beta globulin and to albumin.[30] According to Rosner et al.,[30] under physiological conditions the ratio of distribution for beta globulin to albumin in normal women appears to be 3 to 1. This ratio is increased to about 15 to 1 in women receiving estrogens in large doses and is about 1 to 1 in men. The percent of free estradiol in normal women is about 20% of the total plasma estradiol. As seen earlier, plasma estradiol varies from 50 to 500 $\mu\mu$g/ ml. When radioactive estradiol is injected

into women, about 65% is recovered in the urine, about 10% is recoverable in feces, and the fate of about 25% remains uncertain. About 20% is recoverable in the urine as estradiol, the rest as other metabolites—estrone or estriol.[31] Production rates calculated from urinary metabolites after injection of radioactive estradiol range from 35 to 288 μg/day.[32] Degradation of secreted estrogens apparently occurs in large part in the liver. Fig. 5-6 depicts some of the metabolites of estradiol.[33]

Progesterone is the most important physiologically active progestogen secreted by the ovary; 17-hydroxyprogesterone, Δ^4-3-ketopregnen-20-ol, and possibly 20α-hydroxypregn-4-en-3-one may also be of significance, but further studies are required to determine both their secretory rates and physiological significance (see references listed in reference 14). Pathways of synthesis were discussed in Chapter 2. Progesterone binds well to cortisol-binding globulin and to albumin and circulates, at least in part, in bound form. A specific progesterone-binding globulin similar to estrogen-binding and androgen-binding globulin(s) has not been identified. Production rates range from about 3 mg/24 hr during the follicular phase to about 25 mg during the luteal phase. Metabolic products are numerous (Fig. 5-7). Pregnanediol is a urinary metabolite frequently used as an indicator of progesterone secretion. Of interest is that Riondel et al.[34] found that progesterone concentrations in blood of men were similar to those in ovariectomized women, but that urinary pregnanediol was much higher in the men than in the women. This indicates that urinary pregnanediol is not a unique metabolite of plasma progesterone in men.

Testosterone appears to be the only physiologically important androgen in the human. It is the principal hormone of the testis, but also circulates in detectable amounts in plasma of adult women. Concentrations in women are 370 $\pm$ 10 (SD) $\mu\mu$g/ml of plasma.[35] Plasma from men contains 7300

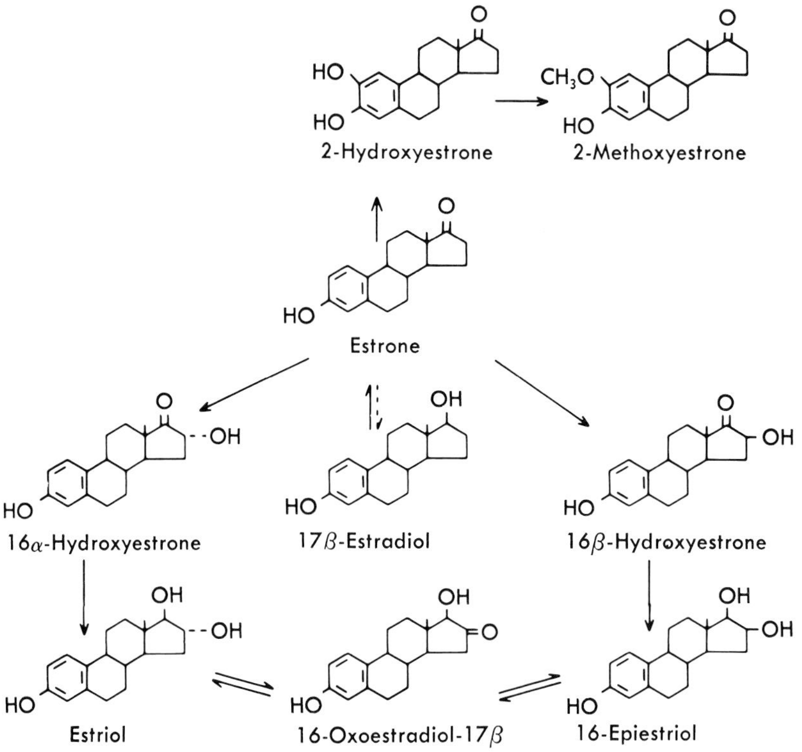

Fig. 5-6. Metabolism of estrogen in the human. All these compounds have been identified in human urine. (From Lloyd, C. W.: The ovaries. In Williams, R. H., editor: Textbook of endocrinology, Philadelphia, 1968, W. B. Saunders Co.)

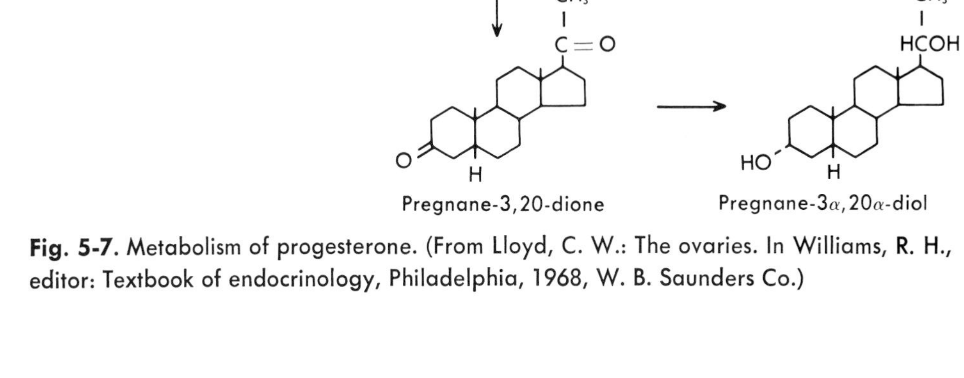

Fig. 5-7. Metabolism of progesterone. (From Lloyd, C. W.: The ovaries. In Williams, R. H., editor: Textbook of endocrinology, Philadelphia, 1968, W. B. Saunders Co.)

$\mu\mu$g $\pm$ 2600 (SD)/ml. Higher values of plasma testosterone are found near midcycle in women.[33] Androstenedione concentrations in women average 1700 $\pm$ 400 $\mu\mu$g/ml and are lower (1200 $\pm$300) in men. Production rates of testosterone in women appear to be about 0.34 mg/day; men synthesize about twenty times that amount. However, the daily production rate of androstenedione is 3.4 mg in women and only 1.4 mg in men. Horton and Tait[36] have demonstrated that a large fraction (40% to 50%) of the testosterone produced in women is derived by conversion of androstenedione to testosterone in peripheral tissues such as skin. Abraham et al.[37] have recently studied relative contributions of the ovary and adrenal. Their results suggest that the ovary contributes about 50% of the overall *production* of testosterone. Blood testosterone

concentrations, however, were only slightly lowered after ovariectomy. These seemingly contradictory statements are explained by the fact that after ovariectomy the metabolic clearance of testosterone is reduced. Thus blood concentrations may be maintained at lower overall secretory rates.

A great deal has been written about *17-ketosteroids*. Almost all of these compounds are derived in women from adrenal secretions. So-called "adrenal androgens" appear to be a nebulous concept; testosterone and its conversion product, dihydrotestosterone, seem to be the only important androgenic steroids. The major portion of adrenal 17-ketosteroid secretion is comprised of dihydroepiandrosterone, a 17-ketosteroid, but not a physiologically important androgen. Androstenedione is another 17-ketosteroid, and it may be readily con-

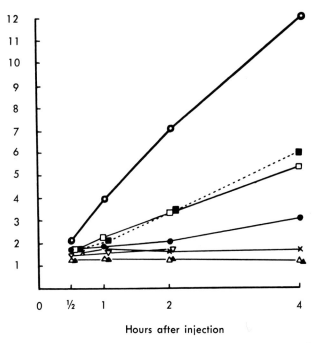

Hours after injection

Fig. 5-8. Ratio of concentrations of radioactivity at various times after injection of tritiated estradiol into rats. The value for the cerebral cortex was taken as 1.0 and used for comparison to other parts of the brain. o, Anterior hypothalamus; ■, posterior part of middle hypothalamus; □, anterior part of middle hypothalamus; •, posterior hypothalamus; ▽, amygdala; x, midbrain; △, cerebellum; ▲, remainder of brain. (From Kato, J., and Villee, C. A.: Endocrinology **80:**567, 1967.)

verted to testosterone in peripheral tissues such as skin. Thus it forms the substrate for androgen formation. The adrenal contribution to secondary sex characteristics is discussed later.

PERIPHERAL BINDING OF FSH, LH, ESTRADIOL, AND PROGESTERONE

It is presently hypothesized by some investigators that the first process of hormone action involves binding to a specific receptor site in the response tissue. Jensen and Jacobson[38] showed that after a single intravenous injection of radioactive estradiol into a female rat, the uterus and vagina concentrated this hormone from blood. Kato and Villee[39] showed that the anterior hypothalamus also concentrated radioactive estradiol. This portion of the brain showed twelve times as much radioactivity as did cerebral cortical tissue (recall that this was the location of the "cyclic center"). Fig. 5-8 depicts data from Kato and Villee's publication. Korenman[40] and Jensen et al.[41] have studied some of the characteristics of binding and the nature of the binding protein in rabbit uterus. This protein appears to bind estrogens avidly and specifically; using it as a binder in a competitive assay system, as little as 10 $\mu\mu$g of estradiol could be quantified, although progesterone, testosterone, and a variety of nonestrogenic steroids failed to bind at all. When it is added *in vitro*, Stumpf,[42] using high-resolution autoradiographic techniques, has been able to show localization of radioactive estradiol in the nucleus of cells in the hypothalamus and pituitary. The binding protein of the uterus appears to be also located in the nucleus. Specific binding of progesterone has not yet been studied. Espeland and Paulsen[43] have recently demonstrated the binding of ^{131}I-LH and FSH to ovarian tissue *in vivo*.

Thus it would appear that tissue binding of estradiol and probably LH and FSH is a very early phenomenon associated with hormone action. It has been hypothesized to be a mandatory prerequisite of hormone action. Wurtman[44] has pointed out that *three alternate hypotheses* are also possible:

1. The estrogen-binding protein may temporarily inactivate the steroid hormone. Sympathetic nerve endings, for example, contain organelles that concentrate ^{3}H-epinephrine. This binding can be blocked, and such blocking does not prevent epinephrine action, but potentiates it.

2. The estrogen-binding protein could merely be acting as a storehouse of estrogen to provide stimulation long after blood estradiol has disappeared.

3. The estrogen receptors may be without physiological significance (although this is unlikely). Continued study of the role of early binding to hormone action is necessary before its significance will be known. Szego and Davis[45] have shown that estradiol results in an increase in adenosine 3',5'-monophosphate (cyclic AMP) in rat uterus within 15 seconds after administration, illustrating that at least very early biochemical actions may precede or occur concomitantly with tissue binding.

METABOLIC ACTIONS OF ESTROGENS, PROGESTOGENS, AND GONADOTROPINS ON TARGET TISSUES
Estrogens

The effects of estrogens on target organs may be dramatic, as they are in the uterus, or more subtle, as they are in adipose tissue. Although a great number of observations on biochemical actions have been made, the exact mode of action and the *initial* step in the action of estrogen remains equivocal. It is clear that estrogen action on uterus results in cellular hypertrophy and hyperplasia with increases in protein synthesis, enzyme activities, and other parameters of cell function. Villee et al. demonstrated some years ago that endometrial isocitrate dehydrogenase activity was markedly increased *in vitro* by estrogen. They postulated that increases in overall cellular activity might be related to these changes. Talalay and Williams-Ashman (see reference 46 for references) linked estradiol dehydrogenase (which catalyzes the interconversion of estradiol and estrone with either DPN or TPN) to the estrogen-sensitive isocitrate dehydrogenase, proposing that the dehydrogenase plays the role of a transhydrogenase by utilizing both DPN and TPN with estradiol as a coenzyme or cosubstrate. This, then, could serve as a stimulus of synthetic activities (for proteins and lipids), which generally require TPNH. However, the significance of these findings remains unclear. Stilbestrol, a potent estrogen, did not affect the activity of isocitrate dehydrogenase nor did it function as a substrate for transhydrogenation (see references 46 and 47 for further references). In 1965, Segal et al.[48] showed that all the morphological actions of estrogens could be produced by local intraluminal application of ribonucleic acid (RNA) from estrogen-stimulated uteri into the uteri of estrogen-deprived animals. Protein synthesis and cell growth changes followed this treatment. Whether this was again the pri-mary action of estrogen (stimulation of RNA synthesis) was unknown. The recent studies mentioned previously of Jensen, Szego, and Korenman and their respective co-workers describe the extremely early effects of estrogen (less than one minute). The possible significance of early binding as a prerequisite of hormone action has been discussed.

The events subsequent to binding are not certain; whether binding is the earliest or is a required action is unknown. The publications of Szego et al. are of particular interest in view of the widespread mediation of cyclic AMP in actions of a variety of hormones (see symposium[48] for some references). Activation of adenyl cyclase[49] with production of cyclic AMP has been implicated in mediating actions of such hormones as glucagon, epinephrine, adrenocorticotropin, thyrotropin, LH, and estrogens (Fig. 5-9). Szego and Davis[45] have shown that the increase in cyclic AMP produced by estradiol within 15 seconds of administration results *subsequently* in enhanced amino acid uptake. The availability of excess amino acids has been shown to pro-

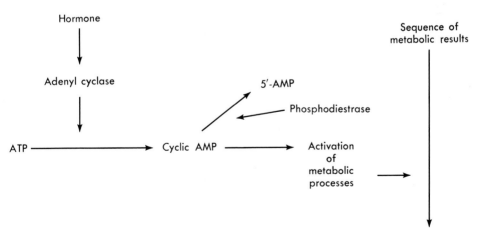

Fig. 5-9. Hypothetical generalized scheme of role of hormonal activation of cyclic AMP as a prerequisite to a variety of hormonal actions. (Modified from Butcher, R. W., and Sutherland, E. W.: The role of cyclic AMP on the lipolytic and antilipolytic actions of hormones and adipose tissue. In Margoulies, M., editor: Protein and polypeptide hormones and metabolism in protein and polypeptide hormones, part I, New York, 1968, Excerpta Medica Foundation.)

mote increased protein synthesis in mammalian liver; an excess may similarly affect protein metabolism in uterus. One might postulate the interrelationship of these early events associated with estrogen action to be as follows (Fig. 5-9). Estradiol has two concurrent early actions: (1) binding to the receptor protein, and (2) activation of adenyl cyclase with resultant production of cyclic AMP. The action of estrogen on metabolic processes is initiated by the latter. However, sustained estradiol effects are mediated by continued release of estradiol from the receptor to give effects long after concentrations of blood bathing the ovary have fallen.

Progestogens

As is shown later, progesterone has rather striking morphological effects on the estrogen-stimulated endometrium. The biochemical effects on this and other mammalian tissues are poorly understood. O'Malley et al.[50] have defined the effects of progesterone on the chick oviduct. This tissue synthesizes a unique protein, avidin (the biotin-binding protein of egg white), upon stimulation with progesterone. Estrogen treatment markedly stimulates oviduct growth and increases the synthesis of nucleic acids and numerous tissue-specific proteins. When a single dose of progesterone is administered to the estrogen-stimulated oviduct, a specific oviduct protein (avidin) is synthesized. These workers showed that progesterone induction of avidin synthesis did not occur via new deoxyribonucleic acid (DNA) synthesis, but was accompanied by increase in RNA synthesis. The RNA synthesis was demonstrable within *10 hours* after progesterone administration. (See the effects of testosterone described in Chapter 6.) These workers suggested that this new RNA might contain the messenger RNA for avidin synthesis. Thus progesterone, as demonstrated in this elegant model system, may alter gene expression to produce new RNA transcription which, in turn, plays a major role in the induction of avidin synthesis. Earlier effects of progesterone, similar to those described for estrogens, have not been described.

FSH and LH

Little information is available on the primary metabolic action of FSH and LH. Mason et al.[51] reported that gonadotropins added *in vitro* increase the corpus luteum synthesis of progesterone in the cow. Armstrong et al.[52] reported that LH added *in vitro* increased glucose uptake by ovaries. Ahrén et al.[53] and Kostyo (see reference 53) found that uptake of the nonmetabolizable amino acid α-aminoisobutyric acid (AIB) into the isolated rat ovary was stimulated by FSH. Ahrén et al.[53] reported that LH added *in vitro* increased isolated ovarian granulosal cells' oxygen utilization, apparently by stimulating succinoxidase activity. All of these observations may well be late effects of these hormones. LH is one of the hormones that stimulate lipolysis *in vitro* in adipose tissue.[48] It is not known whether this action is in any way similar to action on the ovary. Further and definite data must await future studies.

PHYSIOLOGICAL ACTIONS OF THE GONADAL HORMONES

The metamorphosis of a child into an adult woman is caused by estrogen actions on congenitally receptive (XX) tissues. As estrogen concentrations increase, body fat distribution is altered, breast development occurs, skin water content and thickness increase, and subcutaneous fat content increases. Cell division increases in the uterine myometrium, the endometrium increases, and, as discussed earlier, cellular contents of water, electrolyte, and a variety of intracellular synthesized products increase. The vaginal mucosa thickens and vaginal epithelium becomes cornified. Uterine and vaginal secretions are altered: the pH of the vagina is lowered, the vaginal secretion that increases with coitus increases,

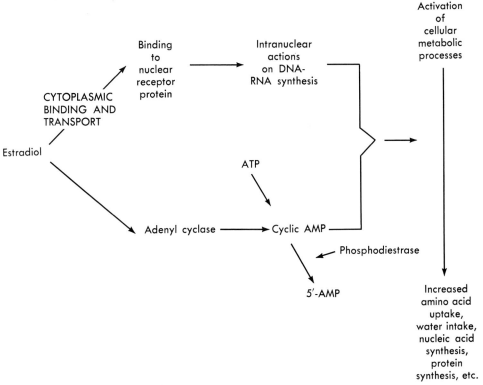

Fig. 5-10. Postulated interaction of early nuclear binding of estradiol and early activation of adenyl cyclase in the uterus. In this scheme, these two early actions of estradiol interact to result in the manifold cellular actions of estradiol.

and cervical mucus becomes copious and watery. After sexual maturation, high estrogen concentrations cause a relative increase in rate of bone maturation; epiphyses close and growth in height ceases. With delays in sexual maturation, height is greater; with early sexual maturation, height is decreased. Fig. 5-10 depicts the changes produced by estrogen in the uterine endometrium. (Puberty is discussed separately in Chapter 7.)

REFERENCES

1. Odell, W. D., Parlow, A. F., Cargille, C. M., and Ross, G. T.: Radioimmunoassay for human follicle-stimulating hormone: physiological studies, J. Clin. Invest. 47:2551, 1968.
2. Odell, W. D., Ross, G. T., and Rayford, P. L.: Radioimmunoassay for luteinizing hormone in human plasma or serum: physiological studies, J. Clin. Invest. 46:248, 1967.
3. Ross, G. T., Odell, W. D., and Rayford, P. L.: Luteinizing hormone activity in plasma during the menstrual cycle, Science 155:1679, 1967.
4. Saxena, B. B., Demura, H., Gandy, H. M., and Peterson, R. E.: Radioimmunoassay of human follicle-stimulating and luteinizing hormones in plasma, J. Clin. Endocr. 28:519, 1968.
5. Runnebaum, B., and Zander, J.: Progesterone in the human peripheral blood in the preovulatory period of the menstrual cycle, Acta Endocr. 55:91, 1967.
6. Neill, J. D., Johansson, E. D. B., Patta, J. K., and Knobil, K.: Relationship between the plasma levels of luteinizing hormone and progesterone during the normal menstrual cycle, J. Clin. Endocr. 27:1167, 1967.
7. Yoshimi, T., and Lipsett, M. B.: The measurement of plasma progesterone, Steroids 11:527, 1968.
8. Strott, C. A., Yoshimi, T., Ross, G. T., and Lipsett, M. B.: Ovarian physiology: relationship between plasma LH and steroidogenesis by the follicle and corpus luteum; effect of HCG, J. Clin. Endocr. 29:1157, 1969.

9. Baird, D. T., and Guevara, A.: Concentration of unconjugated estrone and estradiol in peripheral plasma in nonpregnant women throughout the menstrual cycle, castrate and postmenopausal women and in men, J. Clin. Endocr. 29:149, 1969.

10. Burger, H. B., Brown, J. B., Catt, K. J., Hudson, B., and Stockist, J. R.: Physiological studies on the secretion of human pituitary luteinizing hormone and gonadal steroids. In Margoulies, M., editor: Protein and polypeptide hormones, vol. 2, New York, 1968, Excerpta Medica Foundation.

11. Korenman, S. G., Rao, B. R., Perrin, L. M., and McCollum, T.: Physiological changes during the normal menstrual cycle; comparison between plasma estradiol, basal body temperature, vaginal cytology, and plasma LH, J. Clin. Invest. (Submitted for publication.)

12. Abraham, G. E., and Klaiber, E. L.: Plasma immunoreactive estrogens and LH during the menstrual cycle, Amer. J. Obstet. Gynec. 108:528, 1970.

13. Crooke, A. C., Morell, M., and Butt, W. R.: The recovery of exogenous follicle stimulating hormone from urine. In Rosemberg, E., editor: Gonadotropins, 1968, Los Altos, Calif., 1968, Geron-X, Inc.

14. Odell, W. D., and Swerdloff, R. S.: Progestogen-induced luteinizing and follicle-stimulating hormone surge in postmenopausal women: a simulated ovulatory peak, Proc. Nat. Acad. Sci. U. S. A. 61:529, 1968.

15. Swerdloff, R. S., and Odell, W. D.: Serum luteinizing and follicle stimulating hormone levels during sequential and nonsequential contraceptive treatment of eugonadal women, J. Clin. Endocr. 29:157, 1969.

16. Sawyer, C. H., and Everett, J. W.: Stimulatory and inhibitory effects of progesterone on the release of pituitary hormone in the rabbit, Endocrinology 65:644, 1959.

17. Vande Wiele, R. L., Bogumil, I., Dyrenforth, M., Ferin, R., Jewelewicz, M., Warren, T., Rizkallah, T. H., and Mikhail, G.: Mechanisms regulating the menstrual cycle in women, Recent Progr. Hormone Res. (In press, 1971).

18. Critchlow, V.: Ovulation induced by hypothalamic stimulation in the anesthetized rat, Amer. J. Physiol. 195:171, 1958.

19. Everett, J. W.: Central neural control of reproductive functions of the adenohypophysis, Physiol. Rev. 44:773, 1964.

20. Everett, J. W.: Preoptic stimulative lesions and ovulation in the rat: thresholds and LH release time in late diestros and proestros. In Bajusz, E., and Jasmin, G., editors: Major problems in neuroendocrinology, Basel, Switzerland, 1964, S. Karger Co.

21. Flerkó, B.: Brain mechanisms controlling gonadotrophin secretion and their sexual differentiation. In Lissak, K., editor: Symposium on reproduction, Budapest, 1967, Akadémiai Kiadó.

22. Barraclough, C. A.: Modification in the CNS regulation of reproduction after exposure of prepubertal rats to steroid hormones, Recent Progr. Hormone Res. 22:503, 1966.

23. Terasawa, E., and Timeras, P. S.: Electrical activity during the estrous cycle of the rat: cyclic changes in limbic structures, Endocrinology 83:207, 1968.

24. Barraclough, C. A., and Sawyer, C. H.: Blockade of the release of pituitary ovulating hormones in the rat by chlorpromazine and reserpine. Possible mechanisms of action, Endocrinology 61:341, 1957.

25. Critchlow, V.: Blockade of ovulation in the rat by mesencephalic lesions, Endocrinology 63:596, 1958.

26. David, M. A., Fraschini, F., and Martini, L.: Control of LH secretion: Role of a short feedback mechanism, Endocrinology 78:55, 1966.

27. Corbin, A., and Story, J. C.: "Internal" feedback mechanism: response of pituitary FSH and of stalk-median eminence follicle stimulating hormone-releasing factor to median eminence implants of FSH, Endocrinology 80:1006, 1967.

28. Kohler, P. O., Ross, G. T., and Odell, W. D.: Metabolic clearance and production rates of human luteinizing hormone in pre and postmenopausal women, J. Clin. Invest. 47:38, 1968.

29. Coble, Y. D., Kohler, P. O., Cargille, C. M., and Ross, G. T.: Production rates and metabolic clearance rates of human follicle-stimulating hormone in premenopausal and postmenopausal women, J. Clin. Invest. 48:359, 1969.

30. Rosner, W., Kelly, W. G., Deakins, S. M., and Christy, N. P.: The binding of estrogens and testosterone in human plasmas. In Heyes, R. L., Goswitz, F. A., and Murphy, B. E. P., editors: Radioisotopes in medicine: in vitro studies, 1968, U. S. Atomic Energy Commission, Division of Technical Information.

31. Beer, C. T., and Gallagher, T. F.: Excretion of estrogen metabolites by humans; the fate of small doses of estrone and estradiol-17β J. Biol. Chem. 214:335, 1955.

32. Goering, R. W., Matsuda, S., and Herrmann, W. L.: Estrogen secretion rates in normal women, Amer. J. Obstet. Gynec. 92:441, 1965.

33. Lloyd, C. W.: The ovaries. In Williams, R. H., editor: Textbook of endocrinology, Philadelphia, 1968, W. B. Saunders Co.

34. Riondel, A., Tait, J. F., Tait, S. A., Gut, M., and Little, B.: Estimation of progesterone in human peripheral blood using ^{35}S-thiosemicarbazide, Endocr. 25:229, 1965.

35. Bardin, C. W., and Lipsett, M. B.: Estimation of testosterone and androstenedione in human peripheral plasma, Steroids 9:71, 1967.

36. Horton, R., and Tait, J. F.: Androstenedione production and interconversion rates measured in peripheral blood and studies on the possible site of its conversion to testosterone, J. Clin. Invest. 45:301, 1966.

37. Abraham, G. E., Lobotsky, J., and Lloyd, C. W.: Metabolism of testosterone and androstenedione in normal and ovariectomized women, J. Clin, Invest. 48:696, 1969.

38. Jensen, E. V., and Jacobson, H. I.: Basic guides to the mechanism of estrogen action, Recent Progr. Hormone Res. 18:387, 1962.

39. Kato, J., and Villee, C. A.: Preferential uptake of estradiol by the anterior hypothalamus of the rat, Endocrinology 80:567, 1967.

40. Korenman, S. G.: Comparative binding affinity of estrogens and its relation to estrogenic potency, Steroids 13:163, 1969.

41. Jensen, E. V., DeSombre, E. R., Jungblut, P. W.: Estrogen receptors in hormone-responsive tissues and tumors. In Wissler, R. W., Dao, T. L., and Wood, S., Jr., editors: Endogenous factors influencing host-tumor balance, Chicago, 1967, University of Chicago Press.

42. Stumpf, W. E.: A method for dry high resolution autoradiography and its application to the study of 6, 7- ^{3}H-estradiol-17β in target organs, Ph.D. thesis, Chicago, 1967, The University of Chicago Press.

43. Espeland, D. H., and Paulsen, C. A.: Evidence for specific gonadotrophin "binding sites" in the rat ovary, Clin. Res. (abst.) 17:141, 1969.

44. Wurtman, R. J.: Estrogen receptor: ambiguities in the use of this term, Science 159:1261, 1968.

45. Szego, C. M., and Davis, J. S.: Adenosine 3'5'-monophosphate in rat uterus: acute elevation by estrogen, Proc. Nat. Acad. Sci. 58:1711, 1967.

46. Talalay, P.: Enzymatic mechanisms in steroid metabolism, Physiol. Rev. 37:362, 1951.

47. White, A., Handlen, P., Smith, E. L., and Stetten, D.: Principles of biochemistry, New York, 1959, McGraw-Hill Book Co., Inc.

48. Butcher, R. W., and Sutherland, E. W.: The role of cyclic AMP on the lipolytic and anti-lipolytic actions of hormones and adipose tissue. In Margoulies, M., editor: Protein and polypeptide hormones and metabolism in protein and polypeptide hormones, part I, New York, 1968, Excerpta Medica Foundation.

49. Sutherland, E. W., Øye, I., and Butcher, R. W.: Action of epinephrine and the role of the adenyl cyclase system in hormone action, Recent Progr. Hormone Res. 21:623, 1965.

50. O'Malley, B. W., McGuire, W. L., Kohler, P. O., and Korenman, S. G.: Studies on the mechanism of steroid hormone regulation of synthesis of specific proteins, Recent Progr. Hormone Res. 25:105, 1969.

51. Mason, N. R., Marsh, J. M., and Savard, K.: An action of gonadotropin in vitro, J. Biol. Chem. 236:PC34, 1961.

52. Armstrong, D. T., Kilpatrick, R., and Greep, R. O.: In vitro and in vivo stimulation of glycolysis in prepubertal rat ovary by luteinizing hormone, Endocrinology 73:165, 1963.

53. Ahrén, K. E., Hamberger, A. C., and Hamberger, L. A.: Action of luteinizing hormone in vitro on respiratory enzyme activity of isolated granulosa cells, Endocrinology 77:332, 1965.

CHAPTER 6

Dynamic relationship of the testis to the whole man

CONTROL OF TESTICULAR FUNCTION

As was indicated in earlier chapters, the central nervous system neurohormones and the pituitary hormones controlling gonadal function are identical in men and women. The gonads differ (1) in the predominant hormone secreted and (2) in the fact that gamete formation in men is continual and results in millions to billions per month, whereas in the female usually one gamete per month matures. The maturation of the single gamete requires cyclic central nervous system and pituitary fluctuations; the continual maturation of sperm does not require such cyclic fluctuations. This chapter will attempt to integrate the static considerations presented in Chapters 2 and 4 into a functional dynamic picture.

Central nervous control of pituitary function

Much of the information contained in Chapter 5 pertaining to central nervous system–pituitary interrelations in women forms an important background for understanding such control in men. Fig. 6-1 depicts the central nervous system–pituitary–testicular interrelationships in a diagrammatic fashion. The anatomical pathways are alike in both sexes. The single known difference relates to the so-called "cyclic" and "tonic" areas. Within the hypothalamus, there is only a single active area, corresponding to the "tonic center of Barraclough and Gorski"[1]; the "cyclic center" is not functionally present. The details of activation or inactivation of the "cyclic center" in rodents are discussed in Chapter 7. Some support for the hypothesis that the *human* male does not have a functional cyclic center may be gained from the studies of Odell and Swerdloff. Simulated ovulatory peaks were produced in castrated or postmenopausal women by sequential estrogen and progestogen treatment; no LH-FSH peaks were produced in castrated men or normal men by identical treatment. Possibly a cyclic area is involved in this response and does not function in men. The location of the tonic area in men is unknown but, as was discussed in Chapter 5, it appears to be located in the arcuate-ventromedial nuclear regions of the median eminence in rats (Fig 5-4). This area responds to changes in circulating androgen concentrations for controlling LH (ICSH) secretion. The control of FSH secretion is not well understood. Luteinizing hormone and follicle-stimulating hormone–releasing factors are elaborated by the hypothalamus and these factors in turn control pituitary LH and FSH secretion. In the male, circulating concentrations of LH and FSH appear to be remarkably stable from day to day. Most investigators have found that LH concentrations do not appear to change when measured throughout the day. There may be small changes in FSH diurnally, but even this is uncertain. Data on FSH are conflicting. Saxena et al.[2] and Faiman and Ryan re-

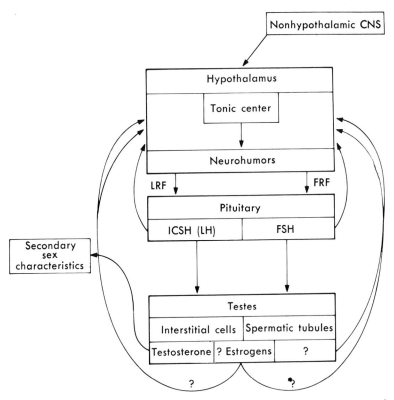

Fig. 6-1. Schematic presentation of the central nervous system–pituitary–testicular inter-relations in men. For details see discussions in Chapters 5 and 6.

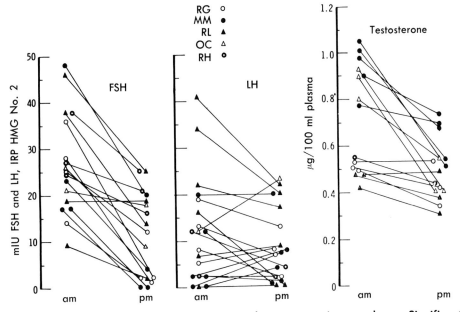

Fig. 6-2. Diurnal changes in plasma FSH, LH, and testosterone in normal men. Significant diurnal variation in FSH and testosterone, but not in LH, was found. (From Saxena, B. B., Demura, H., Gaudy, H. M., and Peterson, R. E.: J. Clin. Endocr. **28**:519, 1968.)

ported small changes; FSH was highest in the morning and lower in the evening. Franchimont, and Swerdloff and Odell failed to find significant changes (see reference 3 for references). Fig. 6-2 depicts data from the studies of Saxena et al., who reported diurnal variations (other references given in references 2 and 4).

Actions of LH and FSH on the testis

Physiological actions. At the testicular level, LH acts to stimulate interstitial cell secretion of testosterone. This potent androgen, the only physiologically important one in men or women, acts in a classic feedback to control LH secretion. Testosterone concentrations in blood are 7300 ± 260 (SD) $\mu\mu$g (picograms)/ml of plasma in men and 370 ± 100 (SD) in women.[4] There are also conflicting data on the pos-

sible diurnal variation of plasma testosterone. Kirschner et al. (1965) and Hudson et al. (1965) could not demonstrate significant diurnal variation, but Rescko and Eiknes (1966) and Southern et al. (1967) (see reference 2 for references) reported a diurnal variation. Administration of LH or human chorionic gonadotropin (HCG), an "LH-like" hormone, results in elevation of plasma testosterone (Fig. 6-3). Conversely, administration of a synthetic androgen (fluoxymesterone) lowers LH concentrations, which in turn results in lower circulating testosterone concentrations.[5] These changes are depicted in Figs. 6-4 and 6-5. Therefore the control of interstitial cell testosterone synthesis and secretion appears to be a straightforward relationship between LH and testosterone.

The control of FSH in men is more com-

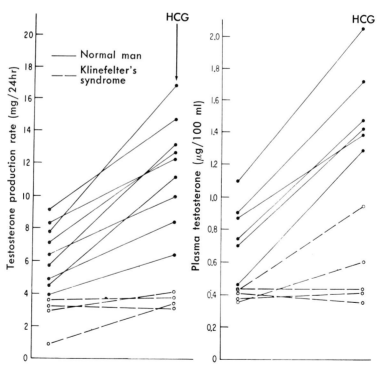

Fig. 6-3. Increase in testosterone production rate and plasma testosterone concentration after treatment with human chorionic gonadotropin (an "LH-like" hormone). (From Lipsett, M. B., Wilson, H., Kirschner, M. A., Korenman, S. G., Fishman, L. M., Sarfaty, G. A., and Bardin, C. W.: Recent Progr. Hormone Res. **22:**245, 1966.)

plex. Fig. 6-6 depicts the results of treatment of normal men with estrogen. LH and FSH concentrations fall but do not become undetectable. Fig. 6-5 shows the results of treatment with a potent oral androgen, fluoxymesterone, wherein LH concentrations fall as previously discussed, but no changes in FSH concentrations are observed.[3] These studies appear to indicate that androgens do not act in a classic feedback with FSH, at least on a short-term basis. Paulsen[6] has shown that when the testes of men are irradiated with about 400 roentgens, azoospermia develops, plasma testosterone (interstitial cell function) and LH excretion remain unchanged, but FSH excretion increases (measured by the ovarian weight augmentation bioassay). Since androgen production was not depressed, these studies indicate that pituitary FSH secretion is controlled in

some manner by the germinal epithelium. Paulsen also indicated that FSH excretion returned to normal as tubular function was restored, although prior to full recovery of the germinal epithelium and prior to restoration of sperm count to normal. The nature of this controlling substance elaborated by the germinal epithelium remains unknown.

Full development of mature sperm requires the effects of both LH and FSH. Woods and Simpson[7] have studied testicular function in hypophysectomized rats in some detail. After regression of the testis caused by hypophysectomy, LH does not act as a complete gonadotropin. It stimulates the atrophic interstitial cell, restoring its morphology to normal, and causes vigorous tubular epithelium proliferation; spermatocytes in meiosis and a few spermatids

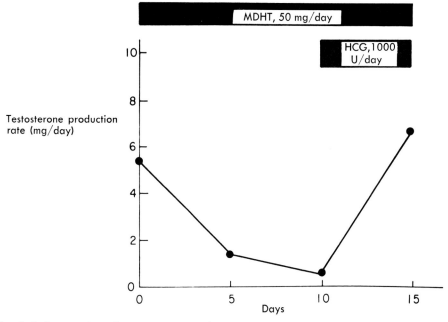

Fig. 6-4. Suppression of testosterone production rate in a normal man by treatment with a potent synthetic androgen, fluoxymesterone (MDHT) (fluoxymesterone is not measured by this specific method used for testosterone). Treatment with chorionic gonadotropin returns testosterone production to normal in spite of continued fluoxymesterone treatment. (From Lipsett, M. B., Wilson, H., Kirschner, M. A., Korenman, S. G., Fishman, L. M., Sarfaty, G. A., and Bardin, C. W.: Recent Progr. Hormone Res. **22:**245, 1966.)

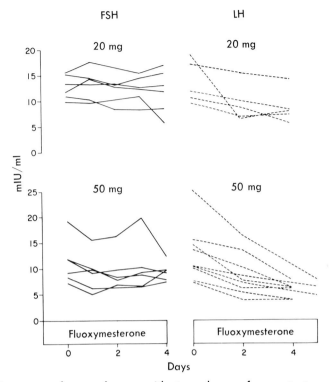

Fig. 6-5. Treatment of normal men with two doses of a potent oral androgen (fluoxymesterone). LH concentrations fell with both doses used; FSH concentrations did not fall with even 50 mg per day treatment. (From Swerdloff, R. S., and Odell, W. D.: Some aspects of the control of secretion of LH and FSH in humans. In Rosemberg, Eugenia, editor: Gonadotropins, 1968, Los Altos, Calif., 1968, Geron-X, Inc.)

occur after 15 days' treatment, but no further advance occurs with injections continued for 2 weeks longer. FSH given alone causes even less repair of testicular tubules. Spermatocytes increase in number, a few meiotic divisions occur, and very young spermatids are visible after 15 and 25 days' treatment. This effect is not sustained and by 28 days no spermatids remain. When FSH is injected with LH, testicular weight and function are restored to normal and mature sperm are present in 40% to 60% of rats at 21 and 28 days.

Interestingly, the addition of growth hormone to LH will increase the sex accessory organ weight response over the effect of treatment with LH and FSH. Growth hormone with LH and FSH treatment results

in even greater stimulation of accessory organs. Spermatogenesis, however, is still not fully developed in all animals after this treatment. Addition of prolactin reportedly results in sperm formation in 100% of the rats. Thus the full restoration of all gonadal function in rats appears to require these four hormones: (1) LH, (2) FSH, (3) growth hormone, and (4) prolactin.

In the human, growth hormone is not required for normal reproduction of either men or women; nor is it required for lactation in women. Rimoin et al.[8] have reported a large number of familially related patients with an isolated deficiency of growth hormone. These subjects are all severely dwarfed, but their reproduction is normal.

Some studies performed in men with hy-

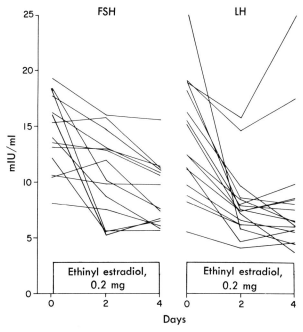

Fig. 6-6. Response to estrogen in males. Suppression of serum FSH and LH concentrations with estrogen treatment of normal men. Concentrations of both hormones fell significantly. (From Swerdloff, R. S., and Odell, W. D.: Some aspects of the control of secretion of LH and FSH in humans. In Rosemberg, Eugenia, editor: Gonadotropins, 1968, Los Altos, Calif., 1968, Geron-X, Inc.)

pogonadism support the findings of Woods and Simpson regarding LH and FSH in the rat. For example, Martin[9] reported a patient with isolated hypogonadotropic hypogonadism having quite low total gonadotropin excretion (mouse uterine weight) and thus probably low secretion of both LH and FSH. Treatment of this patient with 2500 to 5000 IU of chorionic ("LH-like") gonadotropin intravenously twice weekly for 2 months resulted in increase of plasma testosterone from 500 to 6200 $\mu\mu$g/ml (within normal limits for adult men), but azoospermia persisted. After 9 months' treatment azoospermia was still evident. However, after 61 days' treatment with an impure pituitary gonadotropin preparation containing FSH, administered with chorionic gonadotropin, mature sperm were seen for the first time and at a concentration of 140,000/ml.

Another demonstration of the possible interrelations between gonadal steroid secretion and pituitary secretion of FSH and LH in the human results from the effects of clomiphene treatment. Treatment of normal men with clomiphene (an "anti-estrogen" or, in high doses, a weak estrogen) increases the excretion of FSH and LH (determined by bioassay) and the serum LH and FSH (determined by radioimmunoassay). Fig. 6-7 demonstrates these responses and their suppression by fluoxymesterone treatment. It is difficult to completely reconcile these observations with those described previously in this chapter. It is conceivable that small amounts of circulating estrogens are important in controlling FSH secretion and that an "anti-estrogen" might interfere with this control. However, why a potent androgen should abolish this clomiphene action is obscure.

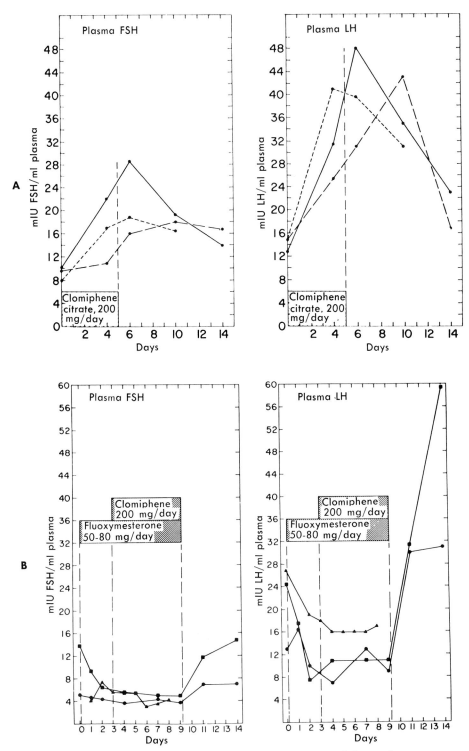

Fig. 6-7. A, Stimulation of FSH and LH secretion in eugonadal men by treatment with clomiphene citrate. **B,** Inhibition of stimulatory effects of clomiphene by simultaneous treatment with fluoxymesterone. (From Cargille, C. M., Ross, G. T., and Bardin, C. W.: Lancet **2:**1298, 1968.)

Biochemical effects of LH. There is relatively little information available on the biochemical effects of LH and FSH on testicular function. Cyclic AMP, discussed in the previous chapter, has been implicated as an intermediary of gonadotropin action[10] in addition to its role in action of other hormones. LH causes an increased conversion of acetate and cholesterol into testosterone by slices of testis incubated *in vitro*.[11] The biochemical actions of FSH on testicular tissue remain unsettled.

Production of estrogens by the testis

A number of studies in humans using isotopically labeled androstenedione and testosterone have shown intraconversion of the two steroids and also conversion to estrone and estradiol. However, several of these studies have measured urinary estrogen metabolites. If conversion occurred primarily in tissues such as liver where further metabolism or conjugation might occur, then blood concentrations of metabolically active estrogens might not change. To study conversions that add significantly to blood concentrations, the free steroid radioactivity in circulating blood must be quantified. Recently Longcope et al.[12] have infused both isotopically labeled androstenedione and testosterone and have measured contributions to blood estrone and to estradiol-17β. It was estimated that androstenedione conversion accounted for 20% of the estrone in males and about 15% in women during the follicular phase of the menstrual cycle. Less than 1.25% of the blood concentrations of the potent estrogen estradiol is derived from testosterone in women. The conversion ratio of testosterone to estradiol is small (0.0015)* and circulating testosterone concentrations are also small. Thus, relative to the large concentrations of estradiol secreted by the ovary, the contribution of testosterone is small. However, this is not

---

* $\dfrac{\text{Estradiol}}{\text{Testosterone}} = 0.0015$

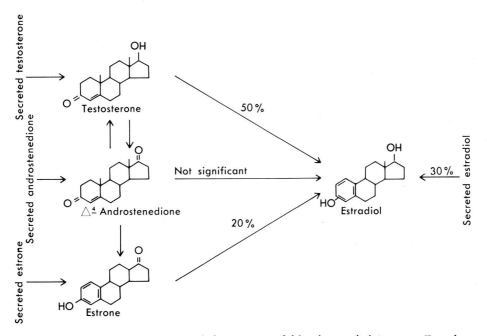

Fig. 6-8. Schematic presentation of the sources of blood estradiol in men. (Based on data from Longcope, Kato, and Horton.[12])

true in men. Testosterone concentrations are much higher, the conversion ratio of testosterone to estradiol is slightly higher (0.0035), and other sources of estradiol are extremely small. Thus conversion of testosterone to estradiol in normal men accounts for about 50% of the circulating estradiol. This is the major source of estradiol in men; about 20% of the estradiol is derived from conversion of estrone (recall that in turn estrone was secreted directly and formed from precursor androgens); and about 30% is derived from directly secreted estradiol.* In men the blood concentrations of estradiol represent the sum of results of a complicated system of interconversions and direct secretions. (For additional discussion and references see reference 12.) Fig. 6-8 depicts these interrelations.

SECRETION, CIRCULATION, AND DEGRADATION OF TESTOSTERONE
Secretion

In men, the great majority (over 90%) of testosterone is derived from testicular secretion.[13] In women, androstenedione is a major source of testosterone; it is converted to testosterone in nonhepatic tissues. This pathway does not represent a significant contribution in men, however. The testes secrete Δ^4-androstenedione and dehydroepiandrosterone in addition to testosterone; relative concentrations in spermatic vein blood are 2.9, 4.5, and 47.9, respectively.[14] The adrenal contribution to testosterone production is shown by adrenocorticotropin (ACTH) treatment. ACTH given to men continuously by a 6-hour intravenous infusion produces no increase in

plasma testosterone. Adrenocorticotropin administration for 4 to 6 days results in approximately a 25% increase in plasma testosterone (mean rise, 1800 $\mu\mu$g/ml).[14] These ACTH studies agree with estimates of Horton and Tait[13] concerning production rates and indicate that under normal circumstances in men, the testes secrete almost all the testosterone. Either the androgenic action of or the conversion of nontestosterone adrenal or testicular steroids to testosterone is of minimal importance in men. Total production of testosterone in men averages 7 mg/24 hr.

Circulation

Testosterone circulates in blood bound predominantly to a beta globulin. Small amounts are bound to inter–alpha globulin (migrates between $\alpha 1$ globulin and $\alpha 2$ globulin) and to albumin.[15] It is uncertain whether two distinct globulins circulate, one binding estradiol and one binding testosterone, or whether one globulin binds both. In competitive inhibition studies, testosterone will compete for binding sites with estradiol and vice versa, suggesting perhaps a single binding substance. This binding to beta globulins is readily reversible.

Degradation

Testosterone is degraded by two pathways in man. One involves the oxidation of the 17β-hydroxyl group to form androstenedione. Androstenedione is further reduced to 5α- and 5β-androstanedione and then to androsterone, isoandrosterone, and 5α- and 5β-androstanediol. The latter three substances are excreted as sulfates and glucuronides. A second pathway involves a direct reduction of testosterone by specific Δ^4-3-ketosteroid 5α- and 5β-reductases (17β-hydroxysteroid 5α- and 5β-reductases) and a specific 3-hydroxysteroid dehydrogenase to 5α- and 5β-androstanediols, which are glucuroconjugated. Fig. 6-9 depicts these pathways. Saez et al.[16] have shown that testosterone sulfate is directly secreted

---

*MacDonald has recently reported that even this 30% figure may be high and that *all* the blood estradiol in men *may* be accounted for by conversion from testosterone and estrone. If this is true, then the testes do not secrete any estradiol directly (MacDonald, P.: 1970 Pfizer symposium. In Strong, J. A., and Baird, D. T., editors: Control of gonadal steroid secretion, Pfizer Medical Monographs 6, in press).

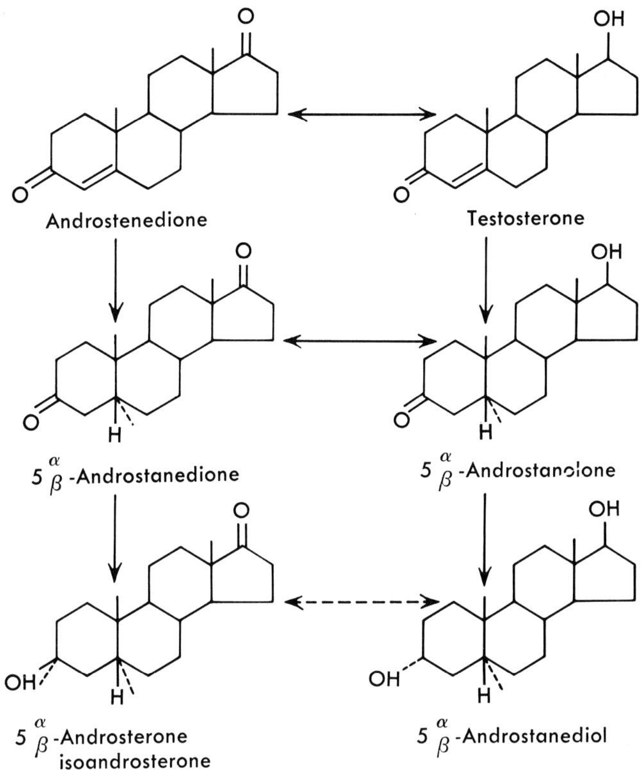

Fig. 6-9. Metabolic pathways for testosterone degradation in the human. (From Mauvais-Jarvis, P., Floch, H. H., and Bercovici, J. P.: J. Clin. Endocr. **28:**460, 1968.)

by the testis and is present in significant amounts in plasma from normal men; the concentration is 1008 ± 490 $\mu\mu g/ml$. Notice that some of the products in Fig. 6-9 are 17-ketosteroids. Testosterone (metabolized to a 17-ketosteroid) and 17-ketosteroids directly secreted by the testis account for approximately 30% of the 17-ketosteroids excreted by normal men. The remainder arises from adrenal "androgen" secretion, mainly dehydroepiandrosterone. Adrenal contributions to puberty and the so-called "adrenarchy" are discussed in Chapter 7.

Testosterone may also be metabolized to estrogens, but this pathway in terms of the fraction of testosterone metabolized is small. The contribution of this metabolic pathway to total estrogen concentrations in men was discussed previously.

ACTIONS OF TESTOSTERONE
Physiological actions

Testosterone produces a variety of effects on a number of body tissues. One of the most dramatic is to stimulate growth and development of the accessory sex organs; the prostate and seminal vesicles are notable examples. The prostate weight bioassay for LH was demonstrated in Chapter 1. In response to testosterone, the external genitalia (penis and scrotum) increase in size and rugal folds appear in the scrotum. Prostatic secretory activity is also stimulated by testosterone. Body hair growth is different from men to women solely because of the effects of testosterone. Pubic hair is more luxuriant in the male pattern (diamond-shaped, with hair extending toward the umbilicus); chest and axillary hair are prominent. On the face, the beard and mustache hair growth is prominent. Temporal recession of scalp hair also occurs under testosterone influence. The voice becomes lower because of enlargement of the larynx and thickening of the vocal cords. At the initiation of increased testosterone secretion at puberty, a marked spurt of height occurs, accompanied by more rapid maturation in bone age and eventual epiphyseal fusion. Increased protein synthesis and decreased amino acid catabolism are observed.[17] Testosterone produces behavioral changes; thus men tend to be more aggressive than women. An interesting study relevant to this in mice was published by Edwards.[18] If male mice are castrated prior to puberty, fighting is rare in adulthood. Testosterone administration to such mice results in arousal of the propensity to fight. However, if adult female mice are treated with testosterone, they do not fight. Edwards reported that testosterone administered to *newborn female* mice altered this response. When these mice reached adulthood and were then treated again with testosterone, fighting females were produced. He thus postulated that an early neural organization occurred, which was stimulated by androgen at birth. The effects of androgen administration on development of the "cyclic" areas of females have been discussed. The possible relationship of these studies to human behavior in men and women is uncertain.

Biochemical actions

Testosterone produces striking growth and morphological change in a variety of target tissues. A large number of studies have been directed toward elucidating the biochemical basis for these changes. Injections of testosterone into immature or castrate animals result in a rapid accumulation of a number of substances—for example, fructose, citric acid, inositol, and glycerophosphorycholine—in the prostate and/or the seminal vesicles (see references listed in 19). These chemicals are found mainly in the glandular lumina where they are stored prior to ejaculation. In spite of a number of studies, there is lack of evidence that testosterone is directly involved in these biochemical reactions. Testosterone treatment of castrate animals increases the rate of oxygen consumption of slices of prostate and seminal vesicles *in vitro,* induces large changes in activity of respiratory and hydrolytic enzymes, and alters the content of nucleic acids. Ritter[20] has shown that 150 μg of testosterone administered to castrate rats will stimulate a rise of NADH within 1 hour, and increase NAD between 1 and 3 hours. Between 1 and 5 hours, the sum of NAD and NADH is constant and is more than twice the sum in both castrate and intact control animals. ATP concentration decreases to a minimum 1 to 2 hours after testosterone, then increases between 2 and 9 hours. Neither actinomycin D* nor puromycin inhibits the NAD response at 7 hours after testosterone injection. Ritter has postulated that androgen activates a redirection of energy metabolism toward a more efficient production of ATP independent of its activation of RNA (discussed later) and protein synthesis.

Williams-Ashman et al. showed that testosterone *in vivo* increases the capacity of prostate ribosomes to incorporate amino acids into proteins. They suggested that testosterone increases the fabrication of certain template RNA. These observations probably explain other studies that report increased amino acid uptake by prostate after testosterone treatment. Testosterone does *not* affect the levels or gross base *composition* of *nuclear* RNA in prostatic tissue, but it does enhance the *template activity* of prostatic nuclear RNA as determined with bacterial and prostatic ribosomal

---

*Actinomycin blocks DNA-directed RNA synthesis. Puromycin blocks protein synthesis at a ribosomal level.

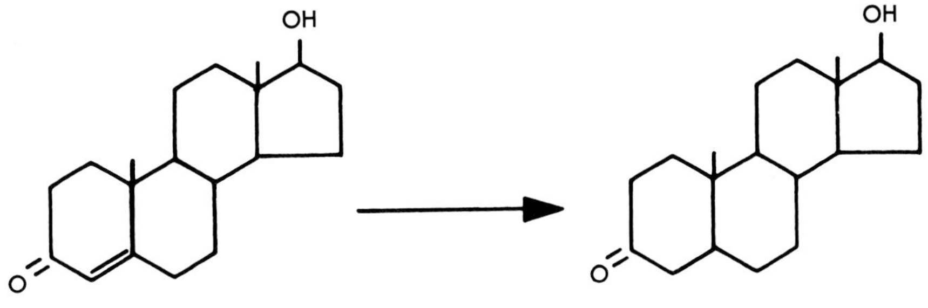

Fig. 6-10. Conversion of testosterone to dihydrotestosterone, the presumed active metabolite of testosterone. This reaction occurs in the nucleus of testosterone-responsive cells.

amino acid incorporating systems (see references listed in 20).

Although these effects are all related to testosterone action, it appears unlikely that any one represents the primary action on target tissue. Sar et al.[21] have recently shown that ^{3}H testosterone or a metabolite is concentrated and bound in nuclei from prostate gland within 30 minutes after testosterone administration *in vivo*.

Within target tissues, testosterone is converted to a 5α-androstan-17β-ol-3-one (dihydrotestosterone) (Fig. 6-10). Dihydrotestosterone is a more potent androgen than testosterone in some assay systems such as the prostate weight assay. (See reference in article 22.) After intravenous injection of testosterone 1, 2, ^{3}H, into rats, dihydrotestosterone can be recovered from prostatic nuclei. Furthermore, Bruchovsky and Wilson found that this is the *only* testosterone metabolite present.[23] An enzyme capable of performing the conversion of testosterone to dihydrotestosterone is present in these nuclei. These same workers[24] have also demonstrated that dihydrotestosterone is bound to nuclear chromatin within 15 minutes (and in greater amounts than testosterone itself) after testosterone administration. Liao and Fang[25] demonstrated the existence of a specific receptor for dihydrotestosterone within prostatic nuclei. The conversion of testosterone to dihydrotestosterone oc-

curs in a variety of tissues, including prostate and skin. The rate of conversion varies with skin obtained from various portions of the body in both sexes of the human. Lowest rates were obtained from miscellaneous areas of the trunk or from the mons; highest rates were obtained in skin from perineal areas such as the labia majora, scrotum, prepuce, and clitoris.

In summary, these findings show that testosterone is rapidly bound and is converted to dihydrotestosterone within cellular nuclei. The dihydrotestosterone formed is bound to a specific nuclear receptor, and subsequent biochemical actions result from action of this steroid.

REFERENCES

1. Barraclough, C. A., and Gorski, R. A.: Evidence that the hypothalamus is responsible for androgen-induced sterility in the female rat, Endocrinology 68:68, 1961.
2. Saxena, B. B., Demura, H., Gaudy, H. M., and Peterson, R. E.: Radioimmunoassay of human follicle stimulating and luteinizing hormones in plasma, J. Clin. Endocr. 28:519, 1968.
3. Swerdloff, R. S., and Odell, W. D.: Some aspects of the control of secretion of LH and FSH in humans. In Rosemberg, Eugenia, editor: Gonadotropins, 1968, Los Altos, Calif., 1968, Geron-X, Inc.
4. Bardin, C. W., and Lipsett, M. B.: Estimation of testosterone and androstenedione in human peripheral plasma, Steroids 9:71, 1947.
5. Lipsett, M. B., Wilson, H., Kirschner, M. A., Korenman, S. G., Fishman, L. M., Sarfaty,

G. A., and Bardin, C. W.: Studies on Leydig cell physiology and pathology: secretion and metabolism of testosterone, Recent Progr. Hormone Res. 22:245, 1966.

6. Paulsen, C. A.: In discussion, p. 163. In Rosemberg, Eugenia, editor: Gonadotropins, 1968, Los Altos, Calif., 1968, Geron-X, Inc.

7. Woods, M. C., and Simpson, M. E.: Pituitary control of the testes of the hypophysectomized rat, Endocrinology 69:91, 1961.

8. Rimoin, D. L., Merimee, T. J., and McKusick, V. A.: Growth hormone deficiency in man: an isolated, recessively inherited defect, Science 152:1635, 1966.

9. Martin, F. I. R.: The stimulation and prolonged maintenance of spermatogenesis by human pituitary gonadotrophins in a patient with hypogonadotrophic hypogonadism, J. Endocr. 38:431, 1967.

10. Marsh, J. M., Butcher, R. W., Savard, K., and Sutherland, E. W.: The stimulatory effect of luteinizing hormone on adenosine-3,-5-monophosphate accumulation in corpus luteum slices, J. Biol. Chem. 241:5436, 1966.

11. Hall, P. F., and Eik-nes, K. B.: The action of gonadotropic hormone on rabbits' testes in vitro, Biochem. Biophys. Acta 63:411, 1962.

12. Longcope, C., Kato, T., and Horton, R.: The conversion of blood androgens to estrogens in normal adult men and women, J. Clin. Invest. 48:2191, 1969.

13. Horton, R., and Tait, J. F.: Androstenedione production and interconversion rates measured in peripheral blood and studies on the possible site of its conversion to testosterone, J. Clin. Invest. 45:301, 1966.

14. Hudson, B., Coghlan, J. P., and Pulmanis, A.: Testicular function in man. In Endocrinology of the testis, vol. 16, 1967, Ciba Foundation's Colloquia on endocrinology.

15. Rosner, W., Kelly, W. G., Deakins, S. M., and Christy, N. P.: The binding of estrogens and testosterone in human plasma. In Hayes, R. L., Goswitz, F. A., and Murphy, B. E. P., editors: Radioisotopes in medicine; in vitro studies, 1968, Atomic Energy Commission.

16. Saez, J. M., Saez, S., and Migeon, C. L.: Identification and measurement of testosterone in the sulfate fraction of plasma of normal subjects and patients with gonadal and adrenal disorders, Steroids 9:1, 1967.

17. Bartlett, P. D.: Rates of protein synthesis, amino acid catabolism, and size of nitrogen pool during nitrogen storage induced with testosterone propionate, and testosterone propionate combined with growth hormone, Endocrinology 52:272, 1953.

18. Edwards, D. A.: Mice: fighting by neonatally androgenized females, Science 161:1027, 1968.

19. Williams-Ashman, H. G., Liao, S., Hancock, R. L., Jurkowitz, L., and Silverman, D. A.: Testicular hormones and the synthesis of ribonucleic acids and proteins in the prostate gland, Recent Progr. Hormone Res. 20:247, 1964.

20. Ritter, C.: NAD biosynthesis as an early part of androgen action, Mod. Pharm. 2:125, 1966.

21. Sar, M., Liao, S., and Stumpf, W. E.: Nuclear concentrations of androgens in rat seminal vesicles and prostate demonstrated by dry mount autoradiography, Endocrinology 86:1008, 1970.

22. Wilson, J. D., and Walker, J. D.: The conversion of testosterone to 5α-androstan-17β-ol-3-one (dihydrotestosterone) by skin slices of man, J. Clin. Invest. 48:371, 1969.

23. Bruchovsky, N., and Wilson, J. D.: The conversion of testosterone to 5α-androstan-17β-ol-3-one by rat prostate in vivo and in vitro, J. Biol. Chem. 243:2012, 1968.

24. Bruchovsky, N., and Wilson, J. D.: The intranuclear binding of testosterone and 5α-androstan-17β-ol-3-one by rat prostate, J. Biol. Chem. 243:5953, 1968.

25. Liao, S., and Fang, S.: Receptor-proteins for androgens and the mode of action of androgens on gene transcription in ventral prostate, Vitamins Hormones 27:17, 1969.

26. Cargille, C. M., Ross, G. T., and Bardin, C. W.: Clomiphene and gonadotropin in men, Lancet 2:1298, 1968.

27. Mauvais-Jarvis, P., Floch, H. H., and Bercovici, J. P.: Studies on testosterone metabolism in human subjects with normal and pathological sexual differentiation, J. Clin. Endocr. 28:460, 1968.

CHAPTER 7

Puberty

The process of sexual maturation—transformation of the sexually immature, infertile child into the sexually mature adolescent—is known as puberty. The physiological and psychological changes occurring throughout this period are complex. Most of the visible changes are due to increased testicular secretion of testosterone in boys or increased ovarian secretion of estrogens in girls. However, as will be discussed, steroid secretion by the adrenal also plays an important role in this body metamorphosis. The changes of puberty occur over a period of 2 to 4 years, usually between ages 11 and 15 in boys and from 9 to 13 in girls. Figs. 7-1 and 7-2 show approximate mean stage of sexual development plotted against age for populations of boys and of girls, respectively.

GONADOTROPIN SECRETION PRIOR TO PUBERTY
Gonadotropin secretion in children

The mechanisms responsible for transformation of the immature hypothalamic-pituitary-gonadal unit into the mature system described in earlier chapters are unknown. Until recently, most physicians have explained these changes as resulting from the *onset* or *initiation* of gonadotropin secretion by the pituitary with resultant gonadal stimulation and gonadal steroid secretion. Several early publications that reported gonadotropin to be undetectable by bioassay in urine from prepubertal children[1-4] supported this concept of puberty. Subsequently, however, investigators studying both large numbers of individual urine samples and large volumes of pooled specimens from children have detected gonadotropins.[5-9] In a study using the mouse uterine weight bioassay, 74% of prepubertal children had detectable gonadotropin in one or more of ten 24-hour urine specimens. Rifkind et al. reported both FSH and LH to be present by specific bioassay in pooled specimens of children's urine; Table 7-1 summarizes from their data the mean excretions of FSH and LH in urine from adult men and prepubertal children of both sexes. When findings were expressed on a surface area or concentration basis and it was assumed that there was no difference in extraction losses, results showed that children excreted less LH and FSH than did the men. The ratio of LH (adult:child) was 10.7:1 and that for FSH was 2.5:1.

In 1967 Odell et al. using the radioimmunoassay for serum LH found that LH was detectable *in serum* of almost all children over the age of 1 year and that concentrations averaged slightly less than in adults, although overlap between the two populations existed.[10] On the basis of these data and a review of published studies in animals, Odell and colleagues suggested that a dynamic hypothalamic-pituitary-gonadal axis exists in children prior to puberty. In support of this hypothesis, Guyda et al.[11] have recently reported that serum of children ages 2 to 9 years with ovarian agenesis contains significantly higher concentrations of LH than serum of normal children (Table 7-2). It is of interest, how-

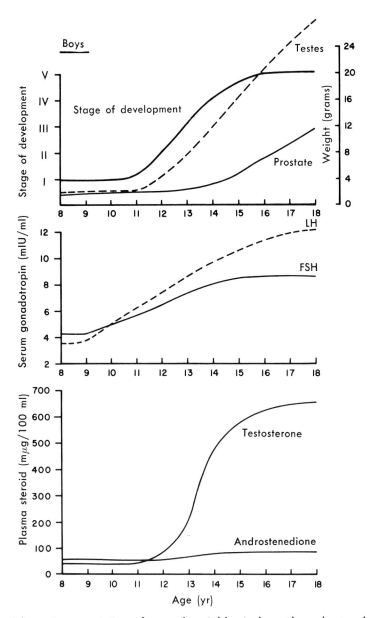

Fig. 7-1. Schematic presentation of several variables in boys throughout puberty. Estimations of prostate and testes weight from Tanner[15]; stage of sexual development from Raiti et al.[12] and Johanson et al.[13]; and testosterone and androstenedione from Frasier et al.[14] All these estimations are approximate averages and represent our interpretations of the reports cited.

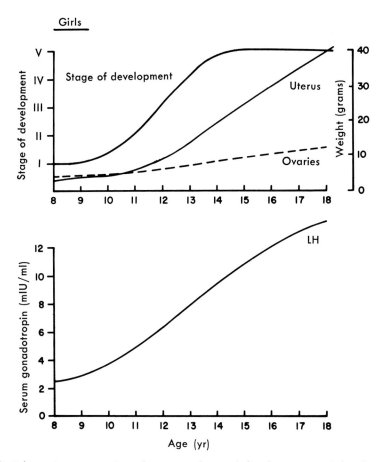

Fig. 7-2. Schematic presentation of a stage of sexual development, weight of uterus and ovaries, and serum gonadotropin concentrations in girls. This diagram represents our interpretation of the published data and shows only approximate values. (From Johanson et al.[13] and Tanner.[15])

Table 7-1. Bioassay measurements of urinary excretion of FSH and LH by prepubertal children and adult men*†

Subjects	FSH (IU, IRP HMG No. 2)			LH (IU, IRP HMG No. 2)		
	Concentration per liter	Concentration per m²/24 hr	Ratio adult:child	Concentration per liter	Concentration per m²/24 hr	Ratio adult:child
Adult	5.6	4.0		4.7	3.3	
			2.5:1			10.7:1
Children	2.2	1.6		0.44	0.31	

*From Rifkind, A. B., Kulin, H. E., and Ross, G. T.: Follicle-stimulating hormone (FSH) and luteinizing hormone (LH) in the urine of prepubertal children, J. Clin. Invest. **46:**1925, 1967.
†An adult was assumed to have an average surface area of 1.8 m² and a urine volume of 1.3 L/day. A child (average age 4) was assumed to have a surface area of 0.7 m² and a urine volume of 0.5 L/day.

ever, that the castrate levels of LH and FSH in children are not as high as levels in castrate adult men and women or postmenopausal women. Thus the fluctuations in gonadotropin levels in children occur within a narrower and lower range.

During puberty, for unknown reasons, the serum gonadotropin concentrations increase gradually to adult levels. In response to this enhanced gonadotropin secretion gonadal hormone secretion is stimulated and sexual development occurs. The pubertal changes in serum concentrations of LH and FSH have recently been described in some detail.[12-14] Our interpretation of these data is shown schematically in Fig. 7-1 for boys and Fig. 7-2 for girls. Average values are shown; changes in a single child followed throughout puberty may, of course, be quite different. Both LH and FSH were detectable at low concentration in boys age 5 or less. These concentrations remained stable through approximately age 9 and then increased progressively over several years, reaching adult values by age 16 to 18. Sexual development (described in Table 7-3) progressed approximately one stage per year for stages II, III, and IV. It required about 2 years to progress from stage IV to V. Changes in sexual stages were paralleled by changes in plasma tes-

tosterone. Androstenedione concentrations did not change significantly during puberty. Correlations between urinary excretion of LH, serum concentrations of LH, and stage of sexual development are shown in Table 7-3. Correlations for FSH are indicated in Table 7-4.

Fig. 7-2 schematically presents serum go-

Table 7-3. Correlations between stage of sexual development, urinary LH excretion, and serum LH concentration*[†]

Stage of sexual development	Urinary LH (mean ± SE)	Serum LH (mean ± SE)
I	2.6 ± 0.2	3.9 ± 0.2
II	8.6 ± 1.3	6.8 ± 0.5
III	12.7 ± 1.8	8.5 ± 0.5
IV	23.0 ± 2.2	9.5 ± 0.6
V	31.1 ± 3.3	11.8 ± 0.8

*Based on data from Guyda, Johanson, Migeon, and Blizzard,[11] and from Raiti, Johanson, Light, Migeon, and Blizzard.[12]
†Urinary LH is given in IU/24 hr as measured by radioimmunoassay, serum LH in mIU/ml, and stage of sexual development in boys throughout puberty as follows: I, preadolescent; II, beginning testicular enlargement and scrotal changes; III, early sexual hair and penile enlargement; IV, sexual hair visible on photograph and further penile and testicular enlargement; V, adult-size genitalia. The particular extraction and concentration technique used for urine and measured by radioimmunoassay gives higher absolute values than obtained by bioassay techniques on kaolin-acetone extracts.[9]

Table 7-2. LH concentrations in prepubertal girls without functioning ovaries as compared with normal girls and women and castrate or postmenopausal women*[†]

Gonadal status	Serum LH (± SE)
Normal girls (age 2 to 9)	2.7 ± 0.3
Girls with ovarian agenesis (age 2 to 9)	4.5 ± 0.3
Normal women (age 19-35)	10.2 ± 0.8‡
Castrate or postmenopausal women	Over 40.0

*Summarized from Guyda, Johanson, Migeon, and Blizzard.[11]
†These data are evidence that a dynamic hypothalamic-pituitary-gonadal axis exists prior to puberty.
‡Except at midcycle.

Table 7-4. Correlations between sexual development and FSH in boys*[†]

Stage of sexual development	Urinary FSH (mean ± SE)	Serum FSH (mean ± SE)
I	2.2 ± 1.1	4.5 ± 0.9
II	4.4 ± 2.5	5.9 ± 1.4
III	7.1 ± 3.0	8.1 ± 3.0
IV	7.8 ± 5.5	8.5 ± 3.2
V	6.9 ± 3.2	7.2 ± 2.2

*From Blizzard, R. M., et al., unpublished data.
†Urinary FSH given in IU/24 hr as measured by radioimmunoassay on extracted and concentrated urine, serum FSH in mIU/ml, and stage of sexual development in boys throughout puberty as defined in Table 7-3.

nadotropin concentrations and stages of sexual development in girls. LH and FSH are also detectable in serum from girls age 5 or less. Concentrations are stable until approximately age 9, then rise steadily over the next 7 years. Menarche occurs at approximately stage IV of sexual development and at an average age of 13.[15]

It is important to emphasize that the data in Figs. 7-2 and 7-3 represent population changes, and concentrations measured in individual children may present a quite different picture. Such data are not available.

Gonadotropin secretion in prepubertal animals

Studies in animals amplify some of these points. In 1929 Kallas[16] studied immature rats joined together in a parabiotic union.* When one of the immature partners was

---

*It appears that polypeptide hormones readily cross the parabiotic union, but steroid hormones do not. The mechanisms are not well understood.

castrated, the other underwent precocious puberty, suggesting that a feedback relationship between the hypothalamus-pituitary control mechanism and the gonad existed and that castration disturbed this relationship. In 1951, Byrnes and Meyer[17] confirmed the findings of Kallas. They also showed that injections of estradiol into the castrate partner could completely prevent the gonadal stimulation caused by castration and at doses *so low that they did not stimulate uterine weight;* Table 7-5 gives some data from this important publication. Johnson[18] joined male and female immature rats to hypophysectomized parabiont partners and was able to demonstrate the presence of LH and FSH in blood by their effects on the gonads and on secondary sex characteristics. Wiesner[19,20] and Price[21] found that neonatal castration of male rats inhibited the growth and development of sex accessory glands.

Odell et al.[22] have recently shown using direct measurements on serum that castration of cattle as young as 1 month of age

Table 7-5. Effects of estradiol on gonadotropin secretion from parabiotic immature rats*†

Group	Treatment	Dose (μg/day)	Number (pairs)	Ovarian weight (mg)	Uterine weight (mg)
Intact-intact	None (noncastrated controls)	0	5	17	——
Castrate-intact	None	0	23	160	52
Castrate-intact	Estradiol administered to castrate	0.0032	2	146	47
		0.0065	2	122	60
		0.0065	1	15	43
		0.009	2	16	45
		0.012	3	25	51
		0.020	3	20	65
		0.025	3	25	135
		0.050	2	29	168

*Modified from Byrnes and Meyer.[17]
†Immature female rats were joined in parabiotic union; the ovaries averaged 17 mg in weight. One partner was castrated, the ovarian weight increased from increased gonadotropin secretion and averaged 160 mg. Varying doses of estradiol were administered to the castrate partner. Inhibition of pituitary gonadotropin secretion, without stimulation of uterine weight occurred when doses of 0.0065 to 0.020 μg/day of estradiol were administered. Lower doses failed to inhibit pituitary secretion; higher doses inhibited pituitary secretion but also stimulated uterine weight. Intact-intact here means immature female rat joined by parabiosis to another immature female rat; castrate-intact means castrate immature female rat joined by parabiosis to intact immature female rat.

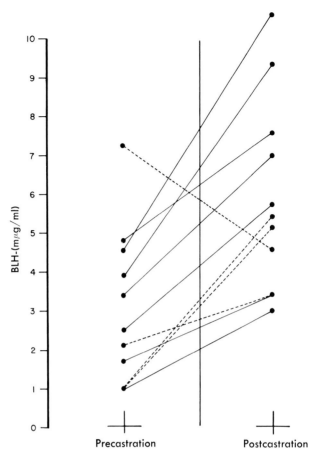

Fig. 7-3. Average LH concentrations in serum from cattle 1 to 4 months of age for 10 days before and 10 days immediately following castration. Lines connect values from single animals: solid lines denote males and dashed lines denote females. Postcastration values are significantly greater than precastration values. (From Odell, W. D., Kiddy, C., and Hescox, M.: Unpublished data.)

will result in small but statistically significant elevations of LH. Fig. 7-3 shows these data. Puberty occurs at about 13 months of age in cattle. These studies in animals also support the concept that a dynamic hypothalamic-pituitary-gonadal axis exists prior to puberty.

Maturation of the ovary prior to puberty

In a number of laboratory animals, the ovary (but not the testis) appears to undergo a series of maturation steps prior to puberty. Prior to this maturation, the ovary

is refractory to gonadotropin, and during this refractory period the dynamic relationship discussed previously does not exist. Three periods of *postnatal* ovarian development have been described in rats, rabbits, and guinea pigs[23]: (1) infantile (in the rat from birth to 10 days of age); (2) early juvenile (in the rat from 10 to 20 days of age); and (3) late juvenile (from 20 days to puberty of 35 to 40 days of age). As discussed in Chapter 3, the proliferation of germ cells and oogonia ceases before birth in mammals.[23] At birth, the rat ovary contains predominantly primary oocytes scattered throughout the cortex, each surrounded by a single layer of flat epithelial cells. At 2 to 3 days in some follicles this epithelium becomes cuboidal, and by the fourth day these follicular cells proliferate to form a layer 4 to 6 cell layers thick. By the sixth day, the ovarian stroma condenses into an undivided theca around each of the growing follicles. During this *infantile period* and parts of the *juvenile period,* a decrease in total number of oocytes and follicles occurs through atresia.

Throughout this infantile period the ovary is unresponsive to exogenous gonadotropins and gonadectomy produces little or no effects on the sex accessories. Interstitial cells with positive histochemical reactions for cholesterol may be seen by the sixth day. By days 10 to 12, other steroids are identifiable by histochemical reactions.

During the *early juvenile period,* the *gonads become sensitive to exogenous gonadotropins.* The interstitial tissue increases in volume and the follicles show rapid growth with proliferation of granulosa cells and increase in antral size. The juvenile period ends when follicles with large antra and a distinct theca appear (18 to 20 days). Gonadectomy results in uterine weight loss when performed during the early or late juvenile stages. The *late juvenile stage* is characterized by continued growth of some follicles and atresia of others. As the volume of interstitial tissue increases and graaffin follicles continue to grow, the late juvenile ovary in the rat differs from the adult ovary only by the lack of corpora lutea.

In summary, in some laboratory animals the prepubertal ovary undergoes an initial maturation process (0 to 10 days in the rat) during which it is refractory to exogenous gonadotropins and during which oophorectomy produces no effects on sex accessory structures.[24] After this maturation is completed, the animal remains sexually immature, but the gonads are capable of increasing their steroid hormone synthesis and secretion in response to exogenous gonadotropins. This maturation process appears to be completed prior to birth in the cow and horse.[23] In children, studies of disease states in which gonadotropins are secreted prematurely by nonpituitary neoplasms or by the pituitary do not appear to show an analagous period of gonadotropin refractoriness. Furthermore, the histological changes described for these three stages in the rat appear to have occurred prior to birth in the human.[24]

Maturation of the testis prior to puberty

Testes of the newborn rat contain small solid nonconvoluted cordlike structures that are the primordia of seminiferous tubules.[23] As the testes mature, the primordia enlarge and become more tortuous, and the cellular elements become organized and stratified as in the adult (Chapter 4); finally, tubular lumina appear. Spermatogenesis *is initiated* in most tubules by 4 to 6 days of age and mature spermatozoa are observed by 35 to 45 days of age. Endocrine function is established at birth in the male rat; as is discussed later, neonatal castration of male rats affects hypothalamic neuroendocrine function involved in gonadotropin secretion. Neonatal castration also inhibits growth and differentiation of accessory glands.[20] The infant rat testis is also sensitive to gonadotropins; Price and Ortiz,[25] for example, demonstrated secretion of androgens in response to gonadotropin treatment between 0 and 6 days of life. This interstitial cell response to gonadotropin also is present at birth. The control of spermatogenesis is more complex and poorly understood even in the adult (Chapter 6).

In summary, an "infantile" period of gonadotropin unresponsiveness comparable to that seen in the female does not appear to exist in male animals,[20,26] and in the human the testes of boys appear to be quite responsive to exogenous gonadotropin.[14] It is possible, however, that unidentified differences in *sensitivity* exist between prepubertal (juvenile) and adult gonads.*

THE HYPOTHALAMUS AND PUBERTY

Pituitary glands of prepubertal rats grafted under the median eminence of hy-

---

*Although it seems certain that a dynamic hypothalamic-pituitary-gonadal relationship exists prior to puberty in rats and cattle, recent studies from the laboratory of one of the authors (William D. Odell) shed some doubt on the importance of the change in sensitivity as the cause of sexual maturation. Swerdloff et al. have shown, using direct FSH and LH measurements by radioimmunoassay in normal *male* rats, that FSH is 300% *higher* in sexually immature than in sexually mature animals. LH in the same animals rises by about 40% during the same period (Swerdloff, Walsh, Jacobs, and Odell: Endocrinology 88:120, 1971). In cattle, Odell et al. showed that LH did not appear to rise significantly during sexual maturation (Odell, Kiddy, and Hescox[22]). Therefore, small increases in gonadotropin secretion, coupled to decreasing hypothalamic sensitivity to gonadal steriod feedback, may not be the sole cause of sexual maturation. Odell et al. have recently shown that ovarian and testicular sensitivity to exogenous purified LH is different in sexually immature and mature animals (Odell, Swerdloff, and Jacobs: Clin. Res., Jan., 1971). Sexually immature animals failed to respond to doses of LH 200 times *greater* than those required in adults. Sensitivity to LH could be induced by prior FSH treatment. Sex accessory stimulation, by testosterone in males and by estradiol in females, was equal in sexually mature and immature rats. In addition, by direct FSH and LH measurement, sensitivity of suppression of LH by administered steroids was equal for LH, and threefold to fourfold greater for FSH in immature versus mature animals. The finding of equal sensitivity for LH suppression is in contradiction to the conclusions from the parabiotic experiments discussed. However, on closer scrutiny, one finds that Byrnes and Meyer[17] measured ovarian weight, mainly an FSH response, and sensitivity of LH suppression was not studied. Studies of gonadal sensitivity to LH and FSH have not yet been done in humans. Thus a complex interplay of (1) changing LH (with or without FSH) secretion, (2) changing gonadal sensitivity to LH (but not FSH), and (3) changes in feedback sensitivity for FSH control appear to produce sexual maturation. The importance of each of these three factors appears to vary from species to species. Read on for additional data concerning the central nervous system and sexual maturation.

pophysectomized adults are stimulated to secrete gonadotropin and function as pituitaries of normal adults.[27] Moreover, testes or ovaries of juvenile rats transplanted to castrate adults also function normally. These studies indicate that the control of puberty does not reside only in the pituitary or the gonad. Donovan and Van der Wertt ten Bosch[28] demonstrated that destructive lesions placed in the base of the rat hypothalamus just caudal to the optic chiasm will advance puberty in rats. In 1967 Ramaley and Gorski[29] reported that, if the neural connections to the medial-basal portion of the hypothalamus were completely severed (this includes the area destroyed in the studies of Donovan and Van der Wertt ten Bosch), precocious puberty resulted and was followed by persistent estrus in females. In these studies a surgical incision was made completely around the medial-basal hypothalamus, and between the thalamic-hypothalamic area, creating an "island" of tissue. These results suggest that extrahypothalamic influences are important in preventing the onset of puberty. Ramaley and Gorski also showed that an anterior incision (anterior deafferentation) would also cause precocious puberty. Thus the anterior hypothalamic input area appears to be of particular importance. Schiavi[30] systematically placed destructive lesions throughout the hypothalamus, and he found that lesions placed anywhere from the suprachiasmatic region and anterior hypothalamus to the premammillary area were effective in producing precocious puberty. This area is similar in location to the island of tissue described by Ramaley and Gorski. Others have shown that continuous light exposure[31] or lesions in the amygdala[32] or stria terminalis[33] also cause precocious puberty. We may thus construct a hypothetical control area for pubertal mechanisms in the rat involving the amygdaloid complex, its radiations via the fornix to the hypothalamus, other extrahypothalamic-neural input via the anterior hypothalamus, and the final common hypothalamic path consisting of the medial-basal portion probably running from the optic chiasm caudally to the mammillary complex. This hypothetical control area probably also exists in the human[34]; precocious puberty is often seen in association with posterior hypothalamic lesions (tumors or congenital abnormalities). However, it is of interest that precocious puberty in humans has not been attributed to localized anterior hypothalamic lesions.

The "male" and "female" hypothalamus

Other studies also demonstrate the hypothalamic origin of gonadotropic control centers prior to puberty. In 1936 Pfeiffer[35] published a very important series of observations. Male rats were castrated at birth, and an ovary was transplanted ectopically (either at birth or at 60 days of age). After puberty, the transplanted ovary functioned normally; that is, the ovary showed cyclic changes typical of those observed in normal females. If similar transplants were made into intact newborn males or into castrated females who also received a testicular graft, cyclic ovarian function was not observed. Pfeiffer concluded that "the hypophysis (pituitary) in the rat at birth is bipotential and capable of being differentiated as either male or female, depending on whether an ovary or testis is present." In addition, he noted that neonatal exposure to testicular secretions destroyed this bipotentiality. Although we now substitute "hypothalamus" for hypophysis, these conclusions are still considered valid. Barraclough and Gorski[36,37] followed up these observations and demonstrated that a single injection of testosterone administered to female rats at birth would cause life-long sterility. The ovaries of these animals exhibited interstitial tissue hypertrophy with numerous large follicles, but no corpora lutea. A similar ovarian picture can be produced in adult female rats by destructive lesions placed in the anterior hypothalamic area.[38] The pituitaries of the androgen-sterilized rats were shown to be low in LH content, and pretreatment with progesterone raised this content. Electrical stimulation of the ventromedial nuclei region of normal female rats results in ovulation, but such stimulation of testosterone-sterilized, progesterone-treated rats failed to produce ovulation. Stimulation in the ventromedial-arcuate area, however, did produce ovulation in the androgen-sterilized, progesterone-treated rats. As discussed in Chapter 5, Barraclough and Gorski postulated that androgens affect the preoptic area.

In summary, in prepubertal rats the hypothalamus appears to be bipotential. In the absence of androgen (with or without ovarian function), the bipotential capabilities persist and will support cyclic pituitary ovarian function. When the rat of either sex is exposed to androgen at or near the time of birth (by injection of testosterone or transplantation of a testis), the cyclic area (preoptic) is functionally destroyed. Hypothalamic differentiation is thus necessary for "female" control. There is little evidence available on this subject in the human. One possible supporting observation is that progesterone administered to estrogen-suppressed castrate or postmenopausal *women* will induce an ovulatory type of LH-FSH peak; similar treatment of castrate or intact *men,* however, produces no such peak. Possibly the "cyclic center" is involved in this progesterone induction phenomenon and is functionally absent in men.

MECHANISMS OF PUBERTY

The previous discussions have been directed toward establishing several points: (1) gonadotropin secretion does occur prior to puberty in children; (2) a functional dynamic hypothalamic-pituitary-gonadal interrelationship has been demonstrated in animals and, recently, in children; (3) extrahypothalamic neural input is important in pubertal control mechanisms; and (4) neonatal androgen secretion in rats has an important influence on the maturation of the neural-gonadal control system although the mechanism of this effect is unknown.

The relevance of points 3 and 4 to children is obscure at this time. A number of investigations have suggested that puberty is associated with an alteration in *sensitivity* of the gonadal steroid feedback system. The low levels of estrogens or androgens secreted prior to puberty become insufficient at the time of puberty to maintain gonadotropin secretion. Increased gonadotropin secretion results and a new equilibrium is reached. No direct evidence for this exists, and mechanisms producing such a postulated change are unknown.*

Certain observations are rather difficult to integrate into a conceptual structure at present. Kupperman et al.[39] reported that treatment of immature rats with a rabbit gonadotropin (LH and FSH) antiserum, between the 10th and 19th days of life, was followed by a pronounced hypersecretion of gonadotropin as evidenced by ovarian and uterine weight increases and vaginal plate opening. Cyclic function began and continued for one or two successive estrus cycles prior to the time vaginal opening occurred in litter mate controls injected with similar volumes of normal rabbit serum. A marked increase in pituitary basophils was also noted. Although one may argue that a compensatory hypersecretion of LH and FSH might temporarily occur in response to antigonadotropin injection (a disturbance of the dynamic prepubertal hypothalamic-pituitary-gonadal axis), it is not possible to explain the subsequent normal

estrus cycles on this basis; precocious puberty had been caused.

Precocious puberty also may be caused by central nervous system lesions. Precocious puberty in boys is almost always associated with central nervous system tumors or hamartomas. These are usually localized to the *posterior* hypothalamic area. Precocious puberty in girls also may be associated with tumors or hamartomas but often occurs in the absence of identifiable central nervous system pathology.

Precocious puberty also may accompany pineal tumors.[40] Such tumors may involve the hypothalamus *or* they may be teratomas that elaborate gonadotropins. In addition, there is evidence suggesting that the pineal may be involved more directly in the timing of puberty.[16] Wurtman et al. in 1959[41] confirmed earlier reports that pineal ablation hastened puberty in rats and showed that pineal extracts prevented the precocious puberty caused by exposure to constant light. Melatonin (5-methoxy-N-acetyltryptamine), a substance which causes aggregation of melanophores in melanocytes of amphibians (a lightening effect opposite to that produced by melanophore-stimulating hormone), is synthesized in the pineal. An enzyme (hydroxyindole-o-methyl transferase) involved in its synthesis is unique to the pineal.[42] The activity of this enzyme is rather specifically increased in pineal tissue of rats by placing the animals in continuous darkness for 6 days. Administration of minute amounts of melatonin (produced by hydroxyindole-o-methyl transferase) over long periods of time to prepubertal rats or exposure to constant darkness delays the onset of puberty. Conversely, exposure of prepubertal rats to constant light hastened the onset of puberty. Interestingly, the pathway for transmission of light to the pineal involves the sympathetic nervous system; superior clinical ganglionectomy abolished the effects of light (for additional reference and discussion see references 43 and 44). The rela-

---

*Additional data bearing on this have been published since completion of this manuscript. Kulin et al. have shown that prepubertal boys and girls will suppress urinary *excretion* of FSH and LH in response to one hundredth or less of the dose of clomiphene required to *stimulate* LH and FSH secretion in adults (Kulin, H. E., Grumbach, M. M., and Kaplan, S. A.: Science **166**:1013, 1969). These are the first direct data in humans suggesting that a difference in sensitivity to feedback suppression may exist.

tion of these observations in rats to pubertal control mechanisms in humans is not completely clear. Rats are nocturnal creatures; humans are not generally considered to be so. Zacharias and Wurtman,[45] in a well-controlled study, have shown that blindness in girls is associated with an age of menarche earlier than normal, an opposite effect to that one would predict from the animal studies. However, the significance of their studies is the demonstration that light can affect the onset of menarche in humans.

THE ADRENARCH

A poorly understood aspect of puberty is the changes associated with alteration of adrenal function. Clinically, it is apparent that women with ovarian hypofunction or ovarian agenesis or men with testicular hypofunction* grow pubic and axillary hair at about the usual age for puberty. Women who suffer from *adrenal* insufficiency lose axillary and pubic hair. For these reasons, the development of axillary and pubic hair at puberty in women is attributed to an "adrenarch" or alteration in adrenal function. Presumably, this hair growth is caused by testosterone predominantly formed in peripheral tissues from androstenedione (Chapter 5). In men, testicular testosterone is much more abundant and forms the support for male patterns of body hair growth. In men, therefore, *hypogonadism* is associated with a decrease in body hair and a "female" type of distribution. The mechanisms of the alterations in adrenal function at puberty remain obscure.

REFERENCES

1. Albert, A.: Human urinary gonadotropin, Recent Progr. Hormone Res. **12**:227, 1956.
2. Wilkins, L.: The diagnosis and treatment of endocrine disorders in childhood and adolescence, ed. 3, Springfield, Ill., 1965, Charles C Thomas, Publisher.
3. Johnsen, S. G.: A clinical routine-method for the quantitative determination of gonadotrophins in 24-hour urine samples. II. Normal values for men and women at all age groups from puberty to senescence, Acta Endocr. **31**:209, 1959.
4. Rosemberg, E.: Urinary gonadotropin excretion measured by the mouse uterine response, employing estrone as the standard reference material, J. Clin. Endocr. **20**:306, 1960.
5. Catchpole, H. R., and Greulich, W. W.: Excretion of gonadotrophic hormone by prepuberal and adolescent girls, J. Clin. Invest. **22**:799, 1943.
6. Brown, P. S.: Human urinary gonadotropins. I. In relation to puberty, J. Endocr. **17**:329, 1958.
7. Fitsclen, W., and Clayton, B. E.: Urinary excretion of gonadotropin with particular reference to children, Arch. Dis. Child. **40**:16, 1965.
8. Kulin, H. E., Rifkind, A. B., Ross, G. T., and Odell, W. D.: Total gonadotropin activity in urine of prepubertal children, J. Clin. Endocr. **27**:1123, 1967.
9. Rifkind, A. B., Kulin, H. E., and Ross, G. T.: Follicle-stimulating hormone (FSH) and luteinizing hormone (LH) in the urine of prepubertal children, J. Clin. Invest. **46**:1925, 1967.
10. Odell, W. D., Ross, G. T., and Rayford, P. L.: Radioimmunoassay for luteinizing hormone in human plasma or serum: physiological studies, J. Clin. Invest. **46**:248, 1967.
11. Guyda, H. J., Johanson, A. J., Migeon, C. J., and Blizzard, R. M.: Serum luteinizing hormone by radioimmunoassay in disorders of adolescent sexual development, Pediat. Res. **3**:533, 1969.
12. Raiti, S., Johanson, A. J., Light, C., Migeon, C. J., and Blizzard, R. M.: Measurement of immunologically reactive follicle stimulating hormone in serum of normal male children and adults, Metabolism **18**:234, 1969.
13. Johanson, A. J., Guyda, H. J., Light, C., Migeon, C. J., and Blizzard, R. M.: Serum luteinizing hormone by radioimmunoassay in normal children, J. Pediat. **74**:416, 1969.
14. Frasier, S., Gafford, F., and Horton, R.: Plasma androgens in childhood and adolescence, J. Clin. Endocr. **29**:1404, 1969.
15. Tanner, J. M.: Growth at adolescence, Oxford, 1962, Blackwell Scientific Publications.
16. Kallas, H.: Puberté précoce por pariparabiose, C. R. Soc. Biol. **100**:979, 1929.
17. Byrnes, W. W., and Meyer, R. K.: The inhi-

---

*The amount of pubic or axillary hair that develops in hypogonadal males is markedly less than that observed in eugonadal males at puberty.

bition of gonadotrophic hormone secretion by physiological doses of estrogen, Endocrinology 48:133, 1951.

18. Johnson, D. C.: The use of non-castrate parabiotic rats for the evaluation of plasma gonadotropins, Acta Endocr. 51:269, 1966.
19. Wiesner, B. P.: Effects of early oophorectomy in rats, J. Physiol. (London) 75:39, 1932.
20. Wiesner, B. P.: The postnatal development of the genital organs in the albino rat, with a discussion of a new theory of sexual differentiation, J. Obstet. Gynaec. Brit. Comm. 41: 867, 1934.
21. Price, D.: An analysis of the factors influencing growth and development of the mammalian reproductive tract, Physiol. Zool. 20: 213, 1947.
22. Odell, W. D., Kiddy, C., and Hescox, M.: Unpublished data.
23. Critchlow, V., and Bar-Sela, M. E.: Control of the onset of puberty. In Martini, L., and Ganong, W. F., editors: Neuroendocrinology, New York, 1967, The Academic Press, Inc.
24. Franchi, L. L., Mandl, A. M., and Zuckerman, S.: The development of the ovary and process of oogenesis. In Zuckerman, S., editor: The ovary, vol. 1, New York, 1962, Academic Press, Inc.
25. Price, D., and Ortiz, E.: The relation of age to reactivity in the reproductive system of the rat, Endocrinology 34:215, 1944.
26. Witschi, E.: Embryology of the ovary. In Grady, H. G., and Smith, D. E., editors: The ovary, Baltimore, 1963, The Williams & Wilkins Co.
27. Harris, G. W., and Jacobsohn, D.: Functional grafts of the anterior pituitary gland, Proc. Roy. Soc. [Biol.] 139:263, 1952.
28. Donovan, B. T., and Van der Wertt ten Bosch, J. J.: The hypothalamus and sexual maturation in the rat, J. Physiol. (London) 147:78, 1959.
29. Ramaley, J. A., and Gorski, R. A.: The effect of hypothalamic deafferentation upon puberty in the female rat, Acta Endocr. 56:661, 1967.
30. Schiavi, R. C.: Effect of anterior and posterior hypothalamic lesions on precocious sexual maturation, Amer. J. Physiol. 206:805, 1964.
31. Fiske, V. M.: Effect of light on sexual maturation; estrous cycles, and anterior pituitary of rat, Endocrinology 29:187, 1941.
32. Elwers, M., and Critchlow, V.: Precocious ovarian stimulation following hypothalamic and amygdaloid lesions in rats, Amer. J. Physiol. 198:381, 1960.
33. Elwers, M., and Critchlow, V.: Precocious ovarian stimulation following interruption of stria terminalis, Amer. J. Physiol. 201:281, 1961.
34. Reichlin, S.: Neuroendocrinology. In Williams, R. H., editor: Textbook of endocrinology, Philadelphia, 1968, The W. B. Saunders Co.
35. Pfeiffer, C. A.: Sexual differences of the hypophyses and their determination by the gonads, Amer. J. Anat. 58:195, 1936.
36. Barraclough, C. A., and Gorski, R. A.: Evidence that the hypothalamus is responsible for androgen-induced sterility in the female, Endocrinology 68:68, 1961.
37. Barraclough, C. A.: Modification in the CNS regulation of production after the exposure of prepubertal rats to steroid hormones, Recent Progr. Hormone Res. 22:503, 1966.
38. Greer, M. A.: Effect of progesterone on persistent vaginal estrus produced by hypothalamic lesions in rat, Endocrinology 53:380, 1953.
39. Kupperman, H. S., Meyer, R. V., and Finerty, J. C.: Precocious gonadal development occurring in immature rats following a short-time treatment with antigonadotropic serum, Amer. J. Physiol. 136:293, 1942.
40. Bailey, P., and Jelliffe, S. E.: Tumors of the pineal body, Arch. Intern. Med. 8:851, 1911.
41. Wurtman, R. J., Altschule, M. D., and Holmgren, E.: Effects of pinealectomy and of a bovine pineal extract in rats, Amer. J. Physiol. 197:108, 1959.
42. Axelrod, J., Maclean, P. D., Albers, R. W., and Weissbach, H.: Regional distribution of methyl transferase enzymes in the nervous system and glandular tissues. In Kety, S., and Elkes, J., editors: Regional neurochemistry, New York, 1961, Pergamon.
43. Cohen, R. A., Wurtman, R. J., Axelrod, J., and Snyder, S. H.: Some clinical, biochemical, and physiological actions of the pineal gland, Ann. Intern. Med. 61:1144, 1964.
44. Wurtman, R. J.: Effects of light and visual stimuli on endocrine function. In Martini, L., and Ganong, W. F., editors: Neuroendocrinology, New York, 1967, Academic Press, Inc.
45. Zacharias, L., and Wurtman, R. J.: Blindness: its relation to age of menarche, Science 144: 1154, 1964.

CHAPTER 8

Sperm and ovum transport

SPERM TRANSPORT

There is a marked reduction in the number of spermatozoa that ascend to the fertilization site in the ampulla of the oviduct. It has been estimated that approximately 66 to 867 million sperm are deposited in the vaginal cavity at the time of ejaculation.[1] Although relatively few studies have been performed in the human, it has been shown that fewer than 100 sperm are present in lumina of the oviducts at the time of fertilization; this represents a reduction in the order of 99.99% of those sperm originally deposited in the vaginal cavity. In the rabbit, although approximately 8 million sperm are initially deposited in the vaginal cavity at the time of ejaculation, only 200 to 500 sperm reach the site of fertilization.[2] Within 3 to 4 hours after ejaculation, maximum numbers of sperm are present in the uterine and oviductal cavities, and this level is maintained for at least 27 hours in the rabbit (Fig. 8-1).

Sperm transport from the vagina to the oviducts is rapid in mammals. Sperm have been found shortly after coitus in the uterine cavity of the mare, sow, and rat.[3,4] In these species, sperm are ejaculated directly into the uterine cavity as the result of relaxation of the cervical opening at the time of coitus. In the rabbit, the time required for sperm passage into the uterus may vary from 1 to 3 hours. In this species, it is likely that the sperm pass through the cervix as a result of their own motility. In the human, sperm are able to penetrate the cervical mucus as a result of the motility of their flagellum, and sperm have been found in the oviducts as early as 30 minutes following coitus.[5]

It has been demonstrated in hysterectomy specimens as well as *in vivo* that when semen is placed at the external cervical os only the morphologically perfect sperm are able to enter the uterine cavity.[6] This has been interpreted to mean that the movements inherent to sperm are responsible for passage through the endocervical canal into the uterine cavity. In the human, the high concentrations of sperm found in the first portion of the ejaculate together with the pumping action of the penis may contribute to the entry of sperm into the cervical mucus.

Both the flagellar motion of the sperm and the muscular activity of the female reproductive tract are involved in the process of sperm migration. The relative importance of these two processes varies among species, and in some species, the sperm enter the oviducts relatively soon after coitus; in others, longer time periods are needed.

The contractility of the uterine and oviductal muscles is usually in the form of segmentation waves,[7,8] rather than peristaltic waves, and this type of wave tends to encourage dispersal of spermatozoa from the point of ejaculation. In the female reproductive tract, the activity of the smooth muscle varies with the phase of the ovarian cycle. At the time of estrus, both the oviductal and uterine muscles show active motility; this is in contrast to the pseudo-

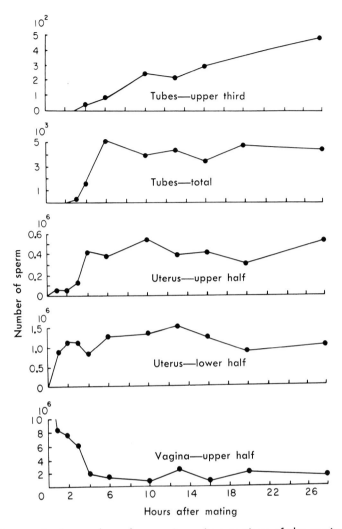

Fig. 8-1. Changes in the number of sperm in various sections of the genital tract relative to time. (From Braden, A. W. H.: Aust. J. Exp. Biol. Med. Sci. **6:**693, 1953.)

pregnant stage when muscular activity is markedly depressed under the influence of progesterone.[9] Experimental work has shown that small dosages of estrogen increase the efficiency of sperm transport in the nonestrus rabbit. In the mare and cow, it has been found that the mating response may enhance uterine contraction, and at estrus the sight of a bull may induce these contractions.

In addition, the ciliary action of the epithelium of the oviducts, uterus, and endocervix plays a minor role in sperm transport; however, since this action produces current formations resulting in a slow movement of fluid together with sperm, it is likely that this mechanism is more important in the elimination of nonfertilizing sperm than the transport of active sperm to the site of fertilization.

Sperm reservoirs which maintain the metabolic activity of sperm include the cervical mucus and the uterine fluid. It is not unusual to find motile sperm in the cervical mucus as long as 3 days or more after an isolated coitus if the woman has a thin watery mucus normally seen at the time of ovulation. Since the cervical mucus is comprised of highly coiled molecules of mucin, the mucus becomes viscid during the luteal and early proliferative phases. At these times, the spaces between the molecules of mucin are narrower than at the time of ovulation when the level of estrogen is relatively high, and a greater amount of energy is required by the sperm to penetrate the viscid mucus. At ovulation, the mucin molecules are straighter and lie farther apart, and the orientation of the molecules determines the lines of direction for the sperm. However, when the alignment of the mucin molecules is relatively straight, the velocity of sperm passing through the mucus is still less than through saline. In the human, sperm have a velocity of 28 μ per second in cervical mucus, compared to 48 μ in saline.[10] The pH factor of cervical mucus may influence fertility in the human patient, and survival of sperm at a pH of 7.5 is more likely than at a lower pH value. In addition, lethal factors have been found in vaginal fluid that immobilize sperm in a matter of seconds; however, these factors have not yet been isolated chemically.

Hormonal changes may influence sperm migration through the female reproductive tract, usually by affecting the quality of the glandular secretions and the activity of the myometrial and oviductal smooth muscle. In a group of pseudopregnant rabbits, no pregnancies resulted following vaginal insemination of sperm. However, when sperm were inseminated into the uterine cavity at the same time in the estrus cycle, a fertilization rate up to 80% was noted, thereby illustrating the importance of changes in cervical mucus. In clinical medicine, when infertile patients show a thick viscid cervical mucus at the time of ovula-tion, the administration of estrogen compounds produces a thinner cervical mucus, thus allowing for the adequate transport of sperm. Myometrial activity is also markedly depressed under the influence of progesterone.

In several species, oxytocin increases the rate of sperm transport. Oxytocin produces a marked response in the contractility of the uterine and oviductal muscles, which in turn facilitates an increase in the number of sperm reaching the ampulla. Following oxytocin injections in the cow, sperm reach the oviducts within several minutes, and estrogen greatly enhances the action of oxytocin on the uterine musculature, whereas progesterone greatly decreases this response.[11] In the rabbit, increased numbers of sperm are found in the uterine and oviductal cavities following oxytocin injections.

Prostaglandin, when present in extremely small amounts, has the unusual property of markedly stimulating uterine smooth muscle activity. This substance stimulates the isolated rat uterus to contract, and the myometrial contractions are proportional to the dosage until a maximal amount of prostaglandin is attained. The isolated human uterus may also be stimulated to contract with very low doses of prostaglandin.

The uterotubal junction is a vital area in regulating the passage of sperm from the uterine cavity to the oviducts. Marked reductions in the numbers of sperm occur at this junction in all mammalian species studied thus far. In the rabbit, only one out of every 1000 to 5000 uterine sperm passes through the uterotubal junction.[2] This junction is a complex anatomical structure with interdigitating bands of smooth muscle that function by obstructing the small lumina between the uterus and oviducts at specific times in the menstrual cycle. In addition, in some species (pig and rabbit), an elaborate arrangement of the epithelium is folded into polypoid excrescences which form a complicated passage. The uterotubal junction becomes distended by large sinuses beneath the epithelium, with the resulting tumescence creating an obstruction to the flow of sperm at the proper time in the cycle. In the human, when the uterotubal sphincter is contracted, a high pressure of gas is required to open the junction into the oviduct. Frequently, more than 100 mm Hg is required to force an opening through the uterotubal junction. In the cow, the resistance of the uterotubal junction to the flow of gas is greatest at the time of estrus. When the musculature of the uterotubal junction was removed by microdissection techniques in the rabbit, an uninhibited ingress and egress of sperm occurred between the uterus and oviduct.[12] Prior to surgery, the uterotubal junction restricted the flow of sperm in the usual fashion. In other studies, live sperm mixed with dead sperm were injected into the rat uterus, and this resulted in the recovery of only live spermatozoa from the oviduct 1 to 14 hours later. The nonmotile sperm remained in the uterus. When sperm of another species such as guinea pig, mouse, or bull were introduced together with rat sperm, the foreign sperm passed through the uterotubal junction (although in reduced numbers) while the homologous sperm were found in the oviducts in the expected numbers.

CAPACITATION OF SPERMATOZOA

Capacitation is a physiological process by which spermatozoa acquire the ability to penetrate the zona pellucida of the recently ovulated ovum. This process is a prerequisite for fertilization in some species, and the biochemical alterations of the sperm required for capacitation occur during the transit through the female genital tract. Although sperm begin to mature while they are stored in the epididymis, neither freshly ejaculated sperm nor sperm removed from the epididymis are capable of fertilizing the egg until they have under-

gone further maturation in the female genital tract. When either ejaculated sperm or epididymal sperm are introduced into oviducts containing freshly ovulated ova in rats and rabbits, the zona pellucida of the ovum is not penetrated during the first several hours until capacitation of the sperm has taken place.[13,14] Capacitation of sperm requires 6 hours in the rabbit, 2 to 3 hours in the rat, approximately 1½ hours in the sheep,[15] and about 3½ hours in the ferret.[16]

Although it has not been proved that sperm capacitation is required in the human or other primates, it has been shown to be essential in the rabbit, rat, mouse, hamster, sheep, and ferret. If this process does occur in humans and other primates, it must require a relatively short period of time. In the monkey, a pronuclear egg was recovered from the oviduct 6 hours after sperm were introduced into the vagina; in the human, sperm incubation with follicular fluid resulted in earlier fertilization than incubation with other media.

Capacitation affects the fertile life of sperm. Sperm begin to age during capacitation, and the duration of their viability diminishes once the process of capacitation has begun. When rabbit spermatozoa were placed in a rat uterus, they remained viable longer than if placed in a rabbit uterus.[17] An exception to this are sperm of the ferret, which retain their fertilizing ability for approximately 120 hours while in the ferret female reproductive tract.

The process of capacitation is not species-specific, and capacitation in heterologous fluids may occur. Hamster sperm may be capacitated with the follicular fluid of the mouse or rat. Rabbit spermatozoa may be partially capacitated with rat follicular fluid. In the rodent, the major fluids involved in capacitation are oviductal and and follicular fluids. Present data indicate that in the process of capacitation, a synergism occurs between the uterine and oviductal fluids. *In vivo* assays carried out in the rabbit indicated that sperm were capacitated in 5 to 6 hours if the oviduct and uterus were in communication; however, this time was increased if the uterotubal junction was occluded. In addition, if the uterus and oviduct were surgically separated, the sperm required about twice as long for capacitation if placed either in the oviduct or uterus.

When sperm were placed in the oviduct of the rabbit several hours prior to ovulation, fertilization occurred approximately 6 hours after ovulation. When epididymal sperm were placed in the rabbit oviduct shortly *after* ovulation, few ova were fertilized; however, if the sperm had been previously incubated in uterine fluid for approximately 6 to 12 hours, most ova were fertilized. In the latter case, it is thought that fertilization took place rapidly, whereas in the former, the aged eggs were impermeable to sperm before the process of capacitation could be completed.

Capacitation of sperm is not limited to the fluids of the female reproductive tract; it may occur in other sites of the body as well. In both the male and female, sperm incubated in a loop of colon, the urinary bladder, the seminal vesicles, and the anterior chamber of the eye have initiated the capacitation process.[18] It is possible that only partial capacitation occurred in these organs, which was then completed in the oviduct; sperm incubated in these organs and transferred to the oviducts were able to fertilize ova in 4 to 6 hours. It has been shown in double-mating experiments with male rabbits of different phenotypic characteristics that the sperm present in the female reproductive tract for the longer period of time have a better chance of fertilizing the ova.

Capacitation of sperm occurs more rapidly during estrus than at other times of the cycle.[19] If the sperm reside in the uterine cavity of an estrus rabbit for 12 hours, all the sperm required for fertilization have been capacitated, and 63% of the ova are fertilized. However, if the same number of

sperm undergo incubation in the uterus of a doe treated with progesterone for 12 hours, a smaller percentage of the ova (2.1%) will be fertilized. Progesterone completely inhibits capacitation in the uterus; however, oviductal fluids are able to capacitate sperm even though the doe may be pseudopregnant or is receiving progesterone. Sperm removed from the uterus of a rabbit that had received leuteinizing hormone 6 hours previously were able to fertilize approximately 93% of the ova; however, when ova were recovered from the uterine cavity of rabbits receiving leuteinizing hormone 12 hours earlier, there was no evidence of fertilization following transfer of sperm.[20]

Capacitation of sperm may be accomplished when sperm are incubated in the oviducts of estrus and pseudopregnant rabbits; however, it occurs more rapidly in the uterine cavity than in the oviducts at estrus. Experimentally, when sperm were incubated in the oviducts for 8 hours after ovulation, approximately 20% of the ova were fertilized; however, when sperm were incubated in the oviducts of ovariectomized animals, the sperm were fully capacitated only after 17 hours.

In the rabbit, capacitation of sperm is reversible and is usually accomplished by incubating capacitated sperm with seminal plasma.[21] When these decapacitated sperm are transferred to the oviduct following ovulation, only a small percentage of the ova are fertilized. The substance which has the property of decapacitating sperm is a protein found in seminal plasma with a molecular weight of 300,000. Sperm that have undergone capacitation and decapacitation may be recapacitated by incubation in the uterine horn. The activity of the decapacitation factor is destroyed by incubation with the enzyme beta amylase, but not by incubation with pronase.

The mechanism of capacitation and the ensuing physiological processes are not fully understood. Several coinciding observations have been made at the time when capacitation normally occurs; however, it is not certain that any of these events are causally related. Both endogenous and exogenous respirations of spermatozoa are higher when sperm are incubated in the uterus than are comparative values for sperm found in freshly ejaculated fluid. There is a fourfold increase of oxygen uptake following sperm incubation in the uterus. It is not yet known whether the acceleration of respiration or the other biochemical reactions within sperm are essential to penetration of the ovum, and further study is required in this area. It has been suggested that a mucolytic enzyme (such as hyaluronidase) may be released by the elevation of the acrosome, thereby allowing sperm to penetrate the zona pellucida. Other theories state that lysosomes are present beneath the acrosome and are released at the time of penetration of the zona pellucida, thereby aiding the passage of sperm into the ooplasm.

FERTILIZING CAPACITY OF SPERM

The capacity of mammalian sperm for the fertilization of ova is limited to a rela-

tively short time period after entry into the female genital tract. The capability of sperm for fertilization is lost earlier than the function of motility, and there is considerable variation among species in the duration of viability of sperm within the female reproductive tract (Table 8-1).[5,22-38] Factors influencing the functional life of sperm within the female reproductive tract include endocrine status of the female, type of fluid (vaginal, cervical, etc.) bathing the sperm, length of time the sperm are in these fluids prior to arrival of the ovum, and numbers of polymorphonuclear leukocytes in the fluids containing sperm.

In general, sperm maintain motility approximately 50% to 100% longer than the ability for fertilization. Therefore, although sperm may be motile, they may not necessarily be capable of fertilization. There is general agreement that if sperm remain in contact with vaginal fluids for even short time periods sperm survival is brief—estimated to be from approximately 1 hour to a maximum of 12 hours. In contrast to the effect of vaginal fluids, sperm survival in the cervical mucus is greater, particularly at the time of ovulation when the mucus

Table 8-1. Duration of fertility and motility of spermatozoa within the female reproductive tract*

Animal	Maximal duration of fertility (hr)	Maximal duration of motility (hr)	References (5 and 22 to 38)
Man	28-48	48-60	Farris, 1950; Rubenstein et al., 1951; Horne and Audet, 1958
Rabbit	30-32	—	Hammond and Asdell, 1926
Guinea pig	21-22	41	Soderwall and Young, 1940
Rat	14	17	Soderwall and Blandau, 1941
Mouse	6	13	Merton, 1939
Ferret	36-48; 126	—	Hammond and Walton, 1934; Chang, 1965
Cow	28-50	96	Laing, 1945; Vanderplassche and Paredis, 1948; Gibbons, 1959
Sheep	30-48	48	Green, 1947; Dauzier and Wintenberger, 1952; Mattner, 1963
Horse	144	144	Day, 1942; Burkhardt, 1949
Bat	135 days	159 days	Wimsatt, 1944

*Modified from Bishop, D. W.: Biology of spermatozoa. In Young, W. C., editor: Sex and internal secretions, vol. 2, Baltimore, 1961, The Williams & Wilkins Co., and Restall, B. J.: Gametes in the female reproductive tract. In McClaren, E. A., editor: Advances in reproductive physiology, vol. 2, London, 1967, Logos Press, Ltd.

is thin and watery. Motile sperm have been found in cervical fluids up to 45 hours after insemination and in some patients have been noted to be sluggishly active up to 110 hours after an isolated coitus. It is believed that the survival time of spermatozoa is shorter in the uterus than in the cervix, and that sperm retain their fertilizing capacity longer in the cervical mucus than in other fluids of the reproductive tract. Few sperm have been found in the human oviduct and there are sparse records of sperm survival in the oviduct.[5,39]

Recent attention has been directed toward the possibility of either lethal or teratogenic effects in sperm that have remained in the female genital tract for relatively long time periods. Although the sperm may be capable of fertilization, it has been suggested that prolonged residence in the female reproductive tract increases the capability of producing either nonviable or abnormal embryos as seen in fowl, as well as through indirect evidence in the human. In contrast, a hibernating female mammal having coitus in the autumn may retain sperm that are motile and capable of fertilization at the time of ovulation in the spring. Long periods of sperm survival have been described in reptiles, with fertile eggs being laid 4 to 5 years after the female was separated from the male.

Sperm survival is partially dependent upon the endocrine state of the animal. When rabbit epididymal sperm were placed in the rat uterus at estrus, they were found to survive for as long as 48 hours; however, when the rats received subcutaneous estrogen, sperm survived no more than 20 hours. Rabbit spermatozoa survive longer in a fluid-filled uterus than in a uterus containing small amounts of fluid. Survival time of sperm in a foreign uterus may be increased when compared to the length of survival in a homologous uterus. The fertility of rabbit sperm incubated in a rat (heterologous) uterus was extended to 50 hours of incubation time as compared to a 25-hour period when incubated in a rabbit (homologous) uterus.[17]

In the rabbit, sperm survival was studied by artificially inseminating does at various time periods prior to ovulation. Although sperm remained motile up to 30 hours after insemination, the sperm's ability to fertilize an ovum and the percentage of fertility fell rapidly after 12 to 15 hours.[24] In 12 to 15 hours after insemination, 91% of the does could be fertilized, but only 60% of the does were fertile at 20 hours and 40% were fertile at 28 hours. In the mouse, the fertilizing ability of sperm remains for approximately 6 hours after coitus and motility ceases around the thirteenth hour. In the rat, fertility decreases at about 10 hours of sperm residence in the reproductive tract with 0% fertility after 14 hours.[26]

FATE OF NONFERTILIZING SPERMATOZOA

The removal of nonfertilizing spermatozoa takes place in several ways. In the human, although some semen may drain from the vagina through the introitus, the majority of sperm and seminal plasma are eliminated within the female reproductive tract. Most sperm are degraded by extracellular digestion resulting from enzymatic activity in the vaginal cavity. Nonfertilizing spermatozoa in the female genital tract may be ingested by polymorphonuclear leukocytes and, more rarely, by mononuclear cells; following this, intracellular degradation of the sperm parts occurs. In addition, a few sperm may traverse the distal portion of the oviduct and become sequestered in the peritoneal cavity where they are degraded by phagocytes.

Sperm penetration of the tissues of the female genital tract has been observed in several lower species. Penetration of the uterine mucosa of the mouse and rat[40] and the oviductal mucosa of the bat has been shown in histological sections.[41]

Within several days after insemination, sperm disappear from the uterine and oviductal cavities in most species. In the human, sperm are rarely found in the uterine cavity more than 30 hours after coitus unless large numbers were deposited in the cervical mucus at the time of insemination.[39] In studies of the mouse and rat, few sperm were found in the uterine cavity 24 hours after coitus. In the mouse, the uterine contents are emptied by cervical dilation and the uterine sperm are expelled back into the vagina for ultimate disposition.[42]

Phagocytosis of nonfertilizing sperm occurs in all species thus far studied. The primary phagocytic cells are polymorphonuclear leukocytes (Fig. 8-2) although, on occasion, mononuclear cells have been observed to phagocytize the spermatozoa (Fig. 8-3). Leukocyte migration into the uterine cavity may be stimulated by the presence of sperm or seminal plasma in the uterine cavity.[43] In most species, there is a time lag between the entry of sperm into the uterine cavity and the emigration of leukocytes; in the mouse, leukocyte emigration and active phagocytosis occur within 4 to 5 hours after insemination, and in the rabbit several hours later.

Sperm phagocytosis takes place in the fluids of the uterine and endocervical cavities. The process is nonspecific and is similar to the phagocytosis of other foreign bodies, such as bacteria.[44] The phagocytic process may be divided into four stages: (1) a preparatory period during which the sperm become nonmotile and may become fragmented, as in the rabbit; (2) a phase of leukocytic adherence and engulfment following biochemical changes on the external cellular surfaces, which enhance phagocytosis; (3) a period of intracellular digestion of sperm. During this stage, either the pseudopodia surround the sperm part or, if no pseudopodia are present, penetration of the plasma membrane takes place. Following ingestion, the sperm part is surrounded by a unilaminar membrane forming a vesicle (phagosome), and the contents of the specific granules of the leuko-

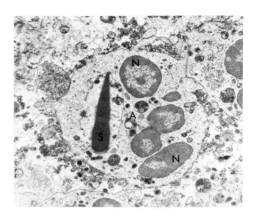

Fig. 8-2. Phagocytosis of a sperm head by a polymorphonuclear leukocyte in the monkey uterus. *S,* Sperm head; *N,* nucleus; *A,* autosome.

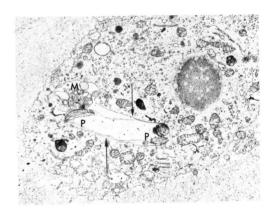

Fig. 8-3. Phagocytosis of the middle piece and principal piece of a human sperm in cervical mucus 12 hours after coitus. *P,* Principal piece; *M,* middle piece. Arrows indicate phagosome membrane.

cyte-containing lysosomes are then discharged into the phagosome containing the sperm. Also during this phase, the proteolytic enzymes then attack and degrade the sperm parts; (4) cytolysis of the fragile leukocyte occurs, with the release of partially digested sperm parts into the extracellular fluid. The leukocytes have a short life-span and undergo cytolysis relatively easily compared to sperm, which are more

Table 8-2. Ovum transport through the oviduct*

Animal	Starting point	Duration in oviduct (days)	Stage at entry into uterus	References (46 to 75)
Man	Ovulation	3	12 cell	Hertig and Rock, 1945; Hertig et al., 1954
Monkey	Ovulation	4	16 cell	Heuser and Streeter, 1941; Lewis and Hartman, 1933
Rabbit	Coitus	3-4	M-B†	Chang, 1948; Chang, 1950; Chang, 1951; Gregory, 1930; Waterman, 1943
Hamster	Coitus	2.5	4-8 cell	Graves, 1945; Venable, 1946
Guinea pig	Coitus	4	4-8 cell	Lewis and Wright, 1935; Sansom and Hill, 1931; Scott, 1937; Squier, 1932
Rat	Coitus	3.5-5	M-B†	Alden, 1948; Lewis and Wright, 1935; MacDonald and Long, 1934; Nicholas, 1942
Mouse	Coitus	3	M-B†	Lewis and Wright, 1935; Snell, 1941
Cow	Ovulation	3-4	8-16 cell	Foley and Reece, 1953; Hamilton and Laing, 1946; Laing, 1945; Winters et al., 1942
Pig	Coitus	4-5	3-4 cell	Green and Winters, 1946; Heuser, 1927; Heuser and Streeter, 1929; Lewis and Wright, 1935
Sheep	Coitus	3-4	—	Assheton, 1898; Clark, 1934; Green and Winters, 1945

*From Beatty, R. A., and Hertig, A. T.: Zygote transport to uterus and implantation time. In Altman, P. L., and Dittmer, D. S., editors: Growth, Bethesda, 1962, Federation of American Societies for Experimental Biology.
†M-B, early morula to late blastocyst.

difficult to destroy. The sperm head, in particular, is difficult to fragment mechanically. The resistance of the sperm nucleus to digestion results from the presence of a keratin-like protein that enmeshes the DNA within the nucleus. When this occurs, the partially digested sperm nucleus is released into the extracellular fluid where it may then be rephagocytized by leukocytes until the digestion process is completed.

Phagocytosis of sperm in the uterine cavity is to a certain extent dependent upon hormonal stimulation. In the rabbit, sperm are phagocytized more rapidly in the uterus during estrus than in the pseudopregnant stage.[45] Migration of leukocytes is more rapid during the period of higher estrogen stimulation than when the uterus is dominated by progesterone.

OVUM TRANSPORT

The physiological transport of ova from the ovarian follicle to the uterine lumen occurs in 3 to 4 days in the human as in most other species (Table 8-2).[46-75] Exceptions include the opossum, in which this process takes 1 day, the dog and cat, which require 6 to 7 days, and the bat, which requires several weeks. The speed of passage through the oviduct is not uniform but varies in different sections, and several stages of ovum transport are usually discernible. In the first stage the egg is transported from the ovarian surface through the ostium in a few minutes. Studies in the rat, using time-lapse photography, have shown that it takes 2 to 5 minutes for the ovum to reach the distal portion of the ampulla[76]; in the rabbit, this process requires 8 to 10 minutes.[77]

After the ovum and the cumulus mass have entered the ostium of the oviducts, contractions of the oviductal musculature result in the transport of the unfertilized ovum through the ampulla. At the ampullary-isthmic junction, further flow of the ovum through the oviduct is temporarily obstructed by a physiological stricture of the musculature. The ovum is normally retained in the ampulla for relatively long periods of time, during which fertilization and cleavage take place (Fig. 8-4). In the rabbit and sheep, the majority of ova are transported to the midportion of the oviduct within 2 hours after ovulation, and the ova remain there for the next 36 hours. The pattern of transport is very similar in all species studied. In primates, it is estimated that the ovum may remain in the ampulla for approximately 3 days before being expelled into the uterine cavity. In most species, the sperm reach the ampulla of the oviduct before the ovum and they wait there for the arrival of the ovum.

Smooth muscle activity and ciliary action in combination are responsible for the regulated movement of ova through the oviduct. Rhythmic contractions of the periovarian area change the ovarian position to the ostium of the oviduct; this phenomenon is important in those species in which contact of the fimbria and the ovarian surface is essential for ovum transport.[7]

Transport of ova through the oviduct is controlled primarily by sphincters of the ampullary-isthmic and the isthmouterine junctions in most mammals. Direct observations show that spontaneous contractions of the oviductal musculature cause a pendular movement of the ova within the

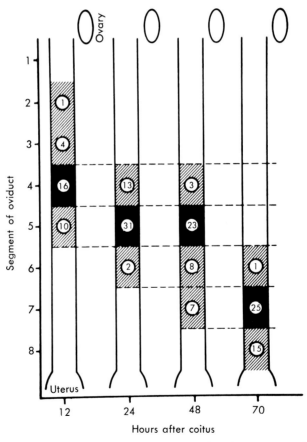

Fig. 8-4. Distribution of rabbit ova during the normal 3-day passage through oviduct. Circled numbers indicate the number of ova recovered from each segment of the oviduct at various times. The stippled segment contained the highest number of ova for each group. (From Greenwald, G. S.: Fertil. Steril. **12**:80, 1961.)

ampulla of the oviduct. These contractions are similar to the smooth muscle response of the small intestine and represent a response to the presence of ova and fluid in the segments of the oviduct.

In some species, cilia arising from the oviductal epithelial cells play a major role in moving the ovum into the ampulla. Fluid from the periovarian area is directed into the ostium by cilia, and current formations facilitate the flow of particulate matter. The cilia appear to be most effective when the ovum is covered by the cumulus mass and mucus. If a particulate body differs in size from that of the cumulus mass, or if the particulate body is not covered with a mucuslike substance, the cilia lose their effectiveness and the particle is not moved through the lumen. In the mouse, ciliated cells present in the ampulla produce a current of oviductal fluid from the distal tip of the oviduct to the ampullary-isthmic junction. In the rabbit, ciliary action is responsible for passage of ova through the distal portion of the ampulla, and segmental contractions are responsible for the movement in the remainder of the ampulla. Stroboscopic experiments have shown that the cilia beat approximately 1200 times per minute.[78] The rapidity of this speed may be altered by hormones, and progesterone increases the

rate of the ciliary beat by approximately 20%.

The last phase of ovum transport through the isthmic portion of the oviduct to the uterine cavity is relatively short. Following fertilization, the pronuclear egg and the subsequent cleavage stages remain in the ampulla for periods of from 1 to 2 days in most species (Fig. 8-2), after which they are released through the ampullary-isthmic junction into the isthmus. Contractions of the isthmic musculature move the eggs into the uterine cavity.

The hormonal control of the ovum transport is dependent upon the absolute amounts of estrogen and progesterone, as well as the ratio of the two substances. However, experimental data are contradictory regarding the precise mechanism of action. The passage of ova into the uterine cavity takes place in approximately the same amount of time (72 to 96 hours) if the ovaries are removed immediately after ovulation in the mouse, rat, and rabbit.[79-81] However, if ovariectomy is performed several weeks previously, transplanted ova enter the uterus more rapidly, usually in 13 to 14 hours, and into the vagina in 14 to 24 hours.[82] In these ovariectomized rabbits, when physiological doses of estrogen are administered at the time of transplantation, most ova are retained in the oviducts,

Table 8-3. Effect of estrogen dose on ovum transport

| Animal | Type of estrogen | Dose of estrogen required | | | References (83 and 84) |
		Accelerated (μg)	Retarded (tube-locking) (μg)	Interruption of pregnancy (80% or more of animals) (μg)	
Rabbit	Depo-estradiol	25	250	—	Greenwald, 1961
Rabbit	ECP*	25	100	50	Greenwald, 1967
Hamster	ECP	100	250	25	Greenwald, 1967
Guinea pig	ECP	50-100	250	10	Greenwald, 1967
Rat	ECP	10+	—	10	Greenwald, 1967

*ECP, estradiol cyclopentylpropionate.

although the mucin coat surrounding the ova is variable in thickness. Increased oviductal and uterine transport of the ova is seen when estrogen is administered for 5 to 10 days prior to transplantation. In the intact animal, both retention of ova in the oviduct and rapidity of transport are directly related to the amount of exogenous estrogen administered. Relatively small doses of estradiol (10 to 100 μg) in the guinea pig, hamster, rabbit, and rat are associated with an acceleration of transport through the oviduct (Table 8-3).[83,84] Higher dosages in the range of 100 to 250 μg result in the retention of ova for long periods in all species except the rat. This retention of ova, termed tube-locking, occurs at the ampullary-isthmic junction rather than at the uterotubal junction.

Progesterone also influences the speed of ovum transport through the oviduct, and in the rabbit, ovum transport is accelerated by the administration of progesterone after mating. Ova are transported from the oviduct to the uterus on the fourth day of pseudopregnancy when the corpus luteum secretes maximal amounts of progesterone. In domestic animals superovulated with gonadotropins, ovum transport is accelerated, presumably as the result of inhibition of the action of estrogen.

In the human, recovery of an ovum and cumulus cells from the lumen of the oviduct during culdoscopy has been de-

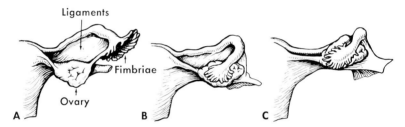

Fig. 8-5. Diagrammatic representation of movements of tube and ovary. **A,** Tube extended; no contraction of musculature of ligaments. **B,** Contraction has started; tube has curved around upper pole of ovary, and fimbriae are in contact with this pole and one side of ovary. **C,** Contraction stronger; fimbriae reach lower ovarian pole and ovary is rotated so as to cause its other side to face ostium abdominale tubae.

Table 8-4. Duration of fertility of the mammalian ovum*

Animal	Duration of fertility (hr)	References (28 and 86 to 97)
Man	6-24	Hartman, 1936
Monkey	23	Lewis and Hartman, 1941
Rabbit	6-8	Hammond, 1934; Braden, 1952; Chang, 1953
Hamster	5	Chang and Fernandez-Cano, 1958
Guinea pig	20	Blandau and Young, 1939; Rowlands, 1957
Rat	12	Blandau and Jordan, 1941
Mouse	8	Runner and Palm, 1953
Ferret	30	Hammond and Walton, 1934
Cow	18-20	Barrett, 1948
Sheep	24	Green and Winters, 1935

*Modified from Blandau, R. J.: Biology of eggs and implantation. In Young, W. C., editor: Sex and internal secretions, vol. 2, Baltimore, 1961, The Williams & Wilkins Co., and Restall, B. J.: Gametes in the female reproductive tract. In McLaren, E. A., editor: Advances in reproductive physiology, vol. 2, London, 1967, Logos Press, Ltd.

scribed.[85] The fimbriated ends of the infundibulum surround a pole of the ovary and cover the apex of the follicle (Fig. 8-5). The protrusion of the ovum from the follicle is a slow process with gradual oozing of the cellular mass onto the fimbria.

Following ovulation, the duration during which the ovum is fertile is relatively short, and the unfertilized mature egg dies soon thereafter. In most species, the sperm are already present in the oviducts and the process of capacitation has begun. Usually, the sperm are ready to penetrate the eggs shortly after ovulation. In most species, passage of ova through the infundibulum to the ampulla takes place in a matter of minutes, or a few hours as in the sheep. In some species, such as the ferret, fertilization takes place in the follicle prior to ovulation with the sperm entering the follicles and penetrating the eggs.

The duration of fertility of mammalian ova has been described in a number of species (Table 8-4).[28,86-97] Delay in fertilization of the ovum has resulted in polyspermy in rats and rabbits.[98,99] In an ovum transplant experiment in rabbits, the unfertilized eggs flushed from the oviduct of a donor rabbit following injection of gonadotropins were then transferred to the oviduct of female rabbits mated with male rabbits 12 hours previously. During a 9-hour period following ovulation, it was found that the ova were all receptive to receiving a sperm through the first 4 hours after ovulation; after that time, the percentage of ova fertilized was reduced progressively to almost no ova fertilized 8 to 9 hours after ovulation. In the guinea pig, the aging of eggs was marked by a decrease in the rate of growth of embryos or by early death of the fertilized egg during the preimplantation period. This effect was noted first at approximately 8 hours following ovulation, and no normal development of the fertilized eggs took place at 20 hours or more following ovulation.

REFERENCES

1. Hotchkiss, R. S.: Fertility in men, Philadelphia, 1944. J. B. Lippincott Co.
2. Braden, A. W. H.: Distribution of sperms in the genital tract of the female rabbit after coitus, Aust. J. Exp. Biol. Med Sci. 6:693, 1953.
3. Mann, T., Polge, C., and Rowson, L. E. A.: Participation of seminal plasma during the passage of spermatozoa in the female reproductive tract of the pig and horse, J. Endocr. 13:133, 1956.
4. Hartman, C. G., and Ball, J.: On the almost instantaneous transport of spermatozoa through the cervix and the uterus in the rat, Proc. Soc. Exp. Biol. Med. 28:312, 1930.
5. Rubenstein, B. B., Strauss, H., Lazarus, M. L., and Hankin, H.: Sperm survival in women; motile sperm in the fundus and tubes of surgical cases, Fertil. Steril. 2:15, 1951.
6. Botella-Llusia, J.: Measurement of linear progression of the human spermatozoa as an index of male fertility, Int. J. Fertil. 1:113, 1955.
7. Blandau, R. J.: Follicular growth, mechanism of ovulation, and egg transport. In Mack, H. C., editor: Symposium on the physiology and pathology of reproduction, Springfield, Ill., 1966, Charles C Thomas, Publisher.
8. Reynolds, S. R. M.: Physiology of the uterus, ed. 2, New York, 1949, Paul B. Hoeber, Inc.
9. Black, D. L., and Asdell, S. A.: Transport through the rabbit oviduct, Amer. J. Physiol. 192:63, 1958.
10. Harvey, C.: The speed of human spermatozoa and the effect on it of various diluents, with some preliminary observations on clinical material, J. Reprod. Fertil. 1:184, 1960.
11. Hays, R. L., and Vandemark, N. L.: Effects of oxytocin and epinephrine on uterine motility in the bovine, Amer. J. Physiol. 172:557, 1953.
12. David, A., Brackett, B. G., and Garcia, C.-R.: Effects of microsurgical removal of the rabbit uterotubal junction, Fertil. Steril. 20:250, 1969.
13. Chang, M. C.: Fertilization in relation to the number of spermatozoa in the fallopian tubes of rabbits, Ann. Ostet. Ginec. 73:918, 1951.
14. Austin, C. R.: Observation on the penetration of the sperm into the mammalian egg, Aust. J. Sci. Res. (s. B) 4:581, 1951.
15. Mattner, P. E.: Capacitation of ram spermatozoa and penetration of the ovine egg, Nature 199:772, 1963.
16. Chang, M. C., and Yanagimachi, R.: Fertilization of ferret ova by deposition of epididymal sperm into the ovarian capsule with spe-

cial reference to the fertilizable life of ova and the capacitation of sperm, J. Exp. Zool. **154**:175, 1963.

17. Bedford, J. M., and Chang, M. C.: Fertilization of rabbit ova in vitro, Nature **193**:808, 1962.

18. Noyes, R. W., Walton, A., and Adams, C. E.: Capacitation of rabbit spermatozoa, J. Endocr. **17**:374, 1958.

19. Chang, M. C.: Capacitation of rabbit spermatozoa in the uterus with special reference to the reproductive phases of the female, Endocrinology **63**:619, 1958.

20. Adams, C. E., and Chang, M. C.: Capacitation of rabbit spermatozoa in the fallopian tube and in the uterus, J. Exp. Zool. **151**:159, 1962.

21. Williams, W. L., Abney, T. O., Chernoff, H. N., Dukelow, W. R., and Pinker, M. C.: Biochemistry and physiology of decapacitation factor, J. Reprod. Fertil., supp. 2, p. 11, 1967.

22. Farris, E. J.: Human fertility and problems of the male, White Plains, N. Y., 1950, Author's press, Inc.

23. Horne, H. W., Jr., and Audet, C.: Spider cells, a new inhabitant of peritoneal fluid: a preliminary report, Obstet. Gynec. **11**:421, 1958.

24. Hammond, J., and Asdell, S. A.: The vitality of spermatozoa in the male and female reproductive tracts, J. Exp. Biol. **4**:155, 1926.

25. Soderwall, A. L., and Young, W. C.: The effect of aging in the female genital tract on the fertilizing capacity of guinea pig spermatozoa, Anat. Rec. **78**:19, 1940.

26. Soderwall, A. L., and Blandau, R. J.: The duration of fertilizing capacity of spermatozoa in the female genital tract of the rat, J. Exp. Zool. **88**:55, 1941.

27. Merton, H.: Studies on reproduction in the albino mouse; the duration of life of spermatozoa in the female reproductive tract, Proc. Roy. Soc. Edinburgh **59**:207, 1939.

28. Hammond, J., and Walton, A.: Notes on ovulation and fertilization in the ferret, J. Exp. Biol. **11**:307, 1934.

29. Chang, M. C.: Fertilizing life of ferret sperm in the female tract, J. Exp. Zool. **158**:87, 1965.

30. Laing, J. A.: Observations on the survival time of the spermatozoa in the genital tract of the cow and its relation to fertility, J. Agric. Sci. **35**:7, 1945.

31. Vanderplassche, M., and Paredis, F.: Preservation of the fertilizing capacity of bull semen in the genital tract of the cow, Nature **162**:674, 1948.

32. Gibbons, R. A.: Physical and chemical properties of mucoids from bovine cervical mucin, Biochem. J. **72**:27, 1959.

33. Green, W. W.: Duration of sperm fertility in the ewe, Amer. J. Vet. Res. **8**:299, 1947.

34. Dauzier, L., and Wintenberger, S.: La vitesse de remontée des spermatozoïdes dans le tractus génital de la brebis, Ann. Inst. Nat. Rech. Agron. No. 1, p. 13, 1952.

35. Mattner, P. E.: Spermatozoa in the genital tract of the ewe. III. The role of spermatozoan motility and of uterine contractions in transport of spermatozoa, Aust. J. Biol. Sci. **16**:877, 1963.

36. Day, F. T.: Survival of spermatozoa in the genital tract of the mare, J. Agric. Sci. **32**:108, 1942.

37. Burkhardt, J.: Sperm survival in the genital tract of the mare, J. Agric. Sci. **39**:201, 1949.

38. Wimsatt, W. A.: Further studies on the survival of spermatozoa in the female reproductive tract of the bat, Anat. Rec. **88**:193, 1944.

39. Moyer, D. L., Rimdusit, S., and Mishell, D. R., Jr.: Sperm distribution and degradation in the human female reproductive tract, Obstet. Gynec. **35**:831, 1970.

40. Austin, C. R.: Fate of spermatozoa in the uterus of the mouse and rat, J. Endocr. **14**:335, 1957.

41. Austin, C. R.: Entry of spermatozoa into the fallopian-tube mucosa, Nature **183**:908, 1959.

42. Blandau, R. J., and Odor, D. L.: The total number of spermatozoa reaching various segments of the reproductive tract in the female albino rat at intervals after insemination, Anat. Rec. **103**:93, 1949.

43. Yanagimachi, R., and Chang, M. C.: Infiltration of leucocytes into the uterine lumen of the golden hamster during the oestrous cycle and following mating, J. Reprod. Fertil. **5**:389, 1963.

44. Moyer, D. L., Legorretta, G., Maruta, H., and Henderson, V.: Elimination of homologous spermatozoa in the female genital tract of the rabbit: a light- and electron-microscope study, J. Path. Bact. **94**:345, 1967.

45. Menge, A. C., Tyler, W. J., and Casida, L. E.: Factors affecting the removal of spermatozoa from the rabbit uterus, J. Reprod. Fertil. **3**:396, 1962.

46. Hertig, A. T., and Rock, J.: Two human ova of pre-villous stage, having developmental age of about seven and nine days respectively, Contrib. Embryol. **31**:65, 1945.

47. Hertig, A. T., Rock, J., Adams, E. C., and Mulligan, W. J.: On preimplantation stages of human ovum: description of 4 normal and 4 abnormal specimens ranging from second to

fifth day of development, Contrib. Embryol. **35**:199, 1954.

48. Heuser, C. H., and Streeter, G. L.: Development of macaque embryo, Contrib. Embryol. **29**:15, 1941.

49. Lewis, W. H., and Hartman, C. G.: Early cleavage stages of the egg of the monkey (Macacus rhesus), Contrib. Embryol. **24**:187, 1933.

50. Chang, M. C.: Transplantation of fertilized rabbit ova: the effect on viability of age, in vitro storage period, and storage temperature, Nature **161**:978, 1948.

51. Chang, M. C.: Probability of normal development after transplantation of fertilized rabbit ova stored at different temperatures, Proc. Soc. Exp. Biol. Med. **68**:680, 1948.

52. Chang, M. C.: Development and fate of transferred rabbit ova or blastocysts in relation to the ovulation time of recipients, J. Exp. Zool. **114**:197, 1950.

53. Chang, M. C.: Fertility and sterility as revealed in the study of fertilization and development of rabbit eggs, Fertil. Steril. **2**:205, 1951.

54. Gregory, P. W.: The early embryology of the rabbit, Contrib. Embryol. **21**:141, 1930.

55. Waterman, A. J.: Studies of normal development of the New Zealand white strain of rabbit; oogenesis; external morphology of the embryo, Amer. J. Anat. **72**:473, 1943.

56. Graves, A. P.: Development of the golden hamster, Cricetus auratus Waterhouse, during the first nine days, Amer. J. Anat. **77**:219, 1945.

57. Venable, J. H.: Pre-implantation stages in the golden hamster (Cricetus auratus), Anat. Rec. **94**:105, 1946.

58. Lewis, W. H., and Wright, E. S.: On the early development of the mouse egg, Contrib. Embryol. **25**:113, 1935.

59. Sansom, G. S., and Hill, J. P.: Observations on the structure and mode of implantation of the blastocyst of Cavia, Trans. Zool. Soc. (London) **21**:295, 1931.

60. Scott, J. P.: The embryology of the guinea pig; a table of normal development, Amer. J. Anat. **60**:397, 1937.

61. Squier, R. R.: The living egg and early stages of its development in the guinea-pig, Contrib. Embryol. **23**:223, 1932.

62. Alden, R. H.: Implantation of the rat egg. III. Origin and development of primary trophoblast giant cells, Amer. J. Anat. **83**:143, 1948.

63. MacDonald, E., and Long, J. A.: Some features of cleavage in the living egg of the rat, Amer. J. Anat. **55**:343, 1934.

64. Nicholas, J. S.: Experimental methods and rat embryos. In Griffith, J. O., Jr., and Farris, E. J., editors: The rat in laboratory investigation, Philadelphia, 1942, J. B. Lippincott Co.

65. Snell, G. D.: Biology of the laboratory mouse, Philadelphia, 1941, The Blakiston Co.

66. Foley, R. C., and Reece, R. P.: Histological studies of the bovine uterus, placenta and corpus luteum, Mass. Agr. Exp. Sta. Bull. **468**:5, 1953.

67. Hamilton, W. J., and Laing, J. A.: Development of the egg of the cow up to the stage of blastocyst formation, J. Anat. **80**:194, 1946.

68. Laing, J. A.: Some factors in the aetiology and diagnosis of bovine infertility, Vet. Rec. **57**:275, 1945.

69. Winters, L. M., Green, W. W., and Comstock, R. E.: Prenatal development of the bovine, Minn. Agric. Exp. Sta. Tech. Bull. **151**:1, 1942.

70. Green, W. W., and Winters, L. M.: Cleavage and attachment stages of the pig, J. Morph. **78**:305, 1946.

71. Heuser, C. H.: Study of implantation of ovum of pig from stage of bilaminar blastocyst to completion of fetal membranes, Contrib. Embryol. **19**:229, 1927.

72. Heuser, C. H., and Streeter, G. L.: Early stages in the development of pig embryos, from period of initial cleavage to time of appearance of limb-buds, Contrib. Embryol. **20**:1, 1929.

73. Assheton, R.: The segmentation of the ovum of the sheep, with observations on the hypothesis of a hypoblastic origin for the trophoblast, Quart. J. Microscop. Sci. **41**:205, 1898.

74. Clark, R. T.: Studies on the physiology of reproduction in the sheep. II. The cleavage stages of the ovum, Anat. Rec. **60**:135, 1934.

75. Green, W. W., and Winters, L. M.: Prenatal development of the sheep, Minn. Agric. Exp. Sta. Tech. Bull. **169**:1, 1945.

76. Harper, M. J. K.: Transport of eggs in cumulus through the ampulla of the rabbit oviduct in relation to day of pseudopregnancy, Endocrinology **77**:114, 1965.

77. Blandau, R. J.: Unpublished data.

78. Borell, U., Nilsson, O., and Westman, A.: Ciliary activity in the rabbit fallopian tube during estrus and after copulation, Acta Obstet. Gynec. Scand. **36**:22, 1957.

79. Whitney, R., and Burdick, H. O.: Effect of massive doses of an estrogen on ova transport in ovariectomized mice, Endocrinology **24**:45, 1939.

80. Alden, R. H.: Aspects of the egg-ovary-ovi-

duct relationship in the albino rat. I. Egg passage and development following ovariectomy, J. Exp. Zool. 90:159, 1942.

81. Adams, C. E.: Egg development in the rabbit: the influence of post-coital ligation of the uterine tube and of ovariectomy, J. Endocr. 16:283, 1958.

82. Noyes, R. W., Adams, C. E., and Walton, A.: The transport of ova in relation to the dosage of oestrogen in ovariectomized rabbits, J. Endocr. 18:108, 1959.

83. Greenwald, G. S.: Species differences in egg transport in response to exogenous estrogen, Anat. Rec. 157:163, 1967.

84. Greenwald, G. S.: A study of the transport of ova through the rabbit oviduct, Fertil. Steril. 12:80, 1961.

85. Doyle, L. L.: Human ova in the fallopian tube, Amer. J. Obstet. Gynec. 95:115, 1966.

86. Hartman, C. G.: The time of ovulation in women, Baltimore, 1936, The Williams & Wilkins Co.

87. Lewis, W. H., and Hartman, C. G.: Tubal ova of the rhesus monkey, Contrib. Embryol. 29:7, 1941.

88. Hammond, J.: The fertilisation of rabbit ova in relation to time; a method of controlling litter size, the duration of pregnancy and weight of young at birth, J. Exp. Biol. 11:140, 1934.

89. Braden, A. W. H.: Properties of the membranes of rat and rabbit eggs, Aust. J. Sci. Res. (s. B) 5:460, 1952.

90. Chang, M. C.: Fertilizability of rabbit germ cells. In Wolstenholme, G. E. W.: Mammalian germ cells, Boston, 1954, Little, Brown & Co.

91. Chang, M. C., and Fernandez-Cano, L.: Effects of delayed fertilization on the development of pronucleus and segmentation of hamster ova, Anat. Rec. 132:307, 1958.

92. Blandau, R. J., and Young, W. C.: The effects of delayed fertilization on the development of the guinea pig ovum, Amer. J. Anat. 64:303, 1939.

93. Rowlands, I. W.: Insemination of the guinea pig by intraperitoneal injection, J. Endocr. 16:98, 1957.

94. Blandau, R. J., and Jordan, E. S.: The effect of delayed fertilisation on the development of the rat ovum, Amer. J. Anat. 68:275, 1941.

95. Runner, M. N., and Palm, J.: Transplantation and survival of unfertilized ova of the mouse in relation to postovulatory age, J. Exp. Zool. 124:303, 1953.

96. Barrett, G. R.: Time of insemination and conception rates in dairy cows (Ph.D. thesis, University of Wisconsin), cited by Blandau, R. J.: Biology of eggs and implantation. In Young, W. C., editor: Sex and internal secretions, Baltimore, 1961, The Williams & Wilkins Co.

97. Green, W. W., and Winters, L. M.: Studies on the physiology of reproduction in the sheep, Anat. Rec. 61:457, 1935.

98. Austin, C. R., and Braden, A. W. H.: An investigation of polyspermy in the rat and rabbit, Aust. J. Biol. Sci. 6:674, 1953.

99. Odor, D. L., and Blandau, R. J.: Incidence of polyspermy in normal and delayed matings in rats of the Wistar strain, Fertil. Steril. 7:456, 1956.

CHAPTER 9

Fertilization

Fertilization is the process of fusion of the male and female gametes with the subsequent union of their nuclear material. It represents the culmination of gamete production in the male and female and the successful transport of these gametes to the site of fertilization. Although most data concerning fertilization have been accumulated in invertebrates, this chapter will include information obtained from mammals whenever possible.

ATTRACTION OF THE SPERMATOZOON TO THE EGG

In species in which external fertilization occurs, spermatozoa move randomly following discharge from the male and collide with the eggs as a matter of chance. Since so many spermatozoa are produced by the male gonads and are discharged into the environment close to the eggs, large numbers of sperm collide with eggs, resulting in a relatively high percentage of egg penetration. In most species studied that depend upon external fertilization, the ripe eggs develop an external sticky surface to which the sperm readily adhere. This adherence process is better observed in some species (such as sea urchins) than in others (such as the starfish), and is dependent upon favorable environmental conditions for its action.

In echinoderms, the layer of jelly surrounding the egg is the source of a substance called fertilizin.[1] Fertilizin is continually released from this jelly and is gradually dissolved into the surrounding sea water after the eggs are laid. The fertilizin molecule is a sulfated glycoprotein which contains more than one active chemical group for the attraction and binding of spermatozoa.[2,3] The molecular weight varies from 300,000 to 1,000,000, depending on the species. The polysaccharide portion of the molecule contains several different monosaccharides and amino acids. The composition of the amino acids and monosaccharides differs according to the species.

On the spermatozoon surface is a complementary substance termed antifertilizin, which is a much smaller molecule than fertilizin and has a molecular weight of about 10,000.[4] Antifertilizin is primarily an acidic protein which may be extracted from the spermatozoon by heating, freezing, thawing, or acidifying the water. The presence of fertilizin and antifertilizin results in the combination of the sperm and egg in a specific manner. This reaction is usually species-specific and reactions between eggs and sperm of different species are much weaker than in the same species even though the two species may be closely related. It has been suggested that the fertilizin-antifertilizin reaction is similar to that which occurs between foreign substances and the serum of immunized animals. The spatial arrangements of the fertilizin molecules are constructed so that the antifertilizin molecules fit closely into their surface. Thus, it is believed, the fertilizin molecules on the egg cytoplasm surface are linked to the antifertilizin molecules on the sperm surface. Fertilizin has been found on the outer surface of the egg plasma membrane, but not within the cytoplasm of sea urchin eggs. When sperm are pretreated with fertilizin, the fertilizing capacity of the spermatozoa is impaired.

In mammals, the presence of a large cumulus mass seen in some mammalian eggs increases the chance of fertilization. This cumulus mass presents a larger target for the sperm to contact, and it is also thought that the spaces between the corona radiata cells orient the sperm movements toward the center of the egg. It has been suggested that there is a perfusion of substances from the surface of the egg in order to attract the sperm; however, the evidence for chemotaxis of sperm is not conclusive.[5] In the human, it has been observed that actively motile sperm show a tendency to concentrate around follicular fluid or fluid from other ovarian cysts.[6] Experiments in mice have shown that those eggs bearing a "t" allele (in contrast to those eggs bearing a "T" allele) were penetrated more frequently by spermatozoa containing a "t" allele. This was interpreted as chemotaxis of the "t" allele–containing egg.[7,8] A study in rats also showed that the frequency of sperm penetration was influenced by the female genotype.

SPERM PENETRATION INTO THE OVUM AND THE ACROSOME REACTION

The plasma membrane of the ripe egg is covered by several investments in most animals. Sperm progression through the egg investments is brought about as follows: In some invertebrates, an enzymatic substance (egg membrane lysin) is released from the acrosome of the spermatozoon as a result of the breakdown of the membranes surrounding the acrosome.[9] This process is referred to as the acrosome reaction. This enzyme facilitates the progression of sperm through the chorion, an investment of varying thickness present just outside the plasma membrane of the eggs of most species. Sperm lysins differ among species;

in species with thick membranes (such as fish or insects) the sperm penetrate the membrane and leave a canal that remains after the sperm has passed into the egg cytoplasm. In other species (such as echinoderms) the jelly coat of the egg may be dissolved by the respired carbon dioxide emitted by the spermatozoa, resulting in acidification of the surrounding water with eventual disappearance of the egg membrane.

In mammals, the zona pellucida and cumulus oophorus (granulosa cells) cover the surface of the egg, and spermatozoa must penetrate these structures before fertilization can take place. The pattern of sperm progression through the egg investments is still a controversial point. On the basis of studying gametes recovered from the oviducts by flushing techniques or the egg fertilized *in vitro*, spermatozoon passage in the zona pellucida has been described in several animals (guinea pigs, rabbits, pigs, and sheep). Rather than penetrate the zona pellucida in the shortest possible distance, the sperm follow a trajectory that is arcuate and may be twice as long as a more direct penetration. Usually, a narrow empty space or split is seen microscopically in the zona pellucida, representing the previous passage of a spermatozoon. It has been suggested that penetration of the zona pellucida may depend upon a lysin contained in the mammalian sperm head located at the level of the inner acrosomal membrane; such a lysin is thought to be present in ram, bull, and rabbit spermatozoa. Rabbit sperm heads observed in the zona pellucida were without an acrosome, with the exception of the posterior portion which seems to be the only portion retained during the acrosome reaction. When the fertilization process is studied by flushing techniques, it is not known with certainty if the sperm seen progressing through the egg envelopes and undergoing an acrosome reaction were responsible for fertilization or whether they

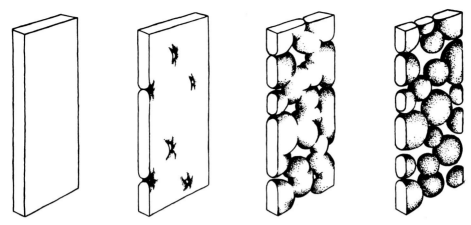

Fig. 9-1. Diagram illustrating inferred stages in the process of vesiculation between two apposed cellular membranes. From the available evidence, it is not certain whether the fourth stage is fully achieved in the sperm acrosome reaction. (From Barros, C., Bedford, J. M., Franklin, L. E., and Austin, C. R.: J. Cell Biol. **34:**C1, 1967.)

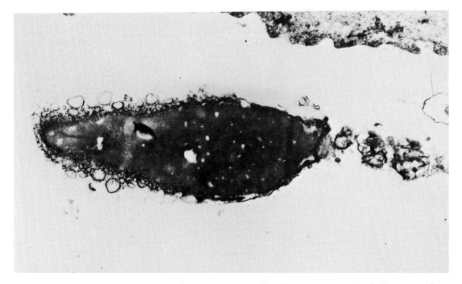

Fig. 9-2. Acrosome reaction in a human sperm showing many vesiculations on the periphery of the nucleus.

were merely supernumerary sperm dislocated from other areas of the oviduct.

The acrosome reaction is thought to be essential for the passage of spermatozoa through the zona pellucida in mammals.[10,11] It involves the vesiculation of the membranes covering the acrosome with a release of acrosomal contents and takes place either before or during the passage of sperm through the cumulus mass. As the reaction develops in mammalian spermatozoa, the outer acrosomal membrane and the adjacent plasma membrane, previously parallel and in close proximity to each other, come into contact and fuse (Fig. 9-1). As this process continues, numerous fenestrations develop

125

between these membranes and eventually extensive vesiculation is seen (Fig. 9-2). It is thought that the contents of the acrosome do not spill out rapidly but escape gradually, allowing continuous action over a period of time. During the acrosome reaction, proteolytic enzymes are believed to be released, which would allow the fertilizing spermatozoon to pass through the cumulus oophorus by digesting the cementing matrix between the cells of the cumulus.

In contrast to the flushing procedures, fertilization studies in the mouse, rabbit, and rat using *in situ* fixation of gametes (a technique that minimizes the manipulation and dislocation of cells) have shown no sperm to be present in the investments of the unfertilized egg.[12] This indicates that passage of sperm through the cumulus cells and zona pellucida is extremely rapid and suggests that the numerous sperm described in the egg envelopes, which are flushed out of the genital organs, are the supernumerary or dislocated sperm. Because of the rapid transit of sperm through the cumulus cells and zona pellucida, it is not known where the acrosome reaction occurs in the mouse; however, when the sperm fuses with the plasma membrane of the ovum, no acrosome is present. The anterior region is covered only by an inner acrosomal membrane which may be surrounded by a row of small vesicles, as in the acrosome reaction.

At the onset of gamete conjugation, the sperm head lies beneath the zona pellucida in the perivitelline space and is in contact with the surface of the egg plasma membrane.[13] Later, some regions of the sperm head become surrounded by the egg plasma membrane and the fusion of membranes occurs shortly thereafter[14] (Figs. 9-3 and 9-4). The postacrosomal cap is the first portion of the sperm to fuse with the plasma membrane of the egg. At this time, the sperm tail is usually located entirely in the perivitelline space. When the corti-

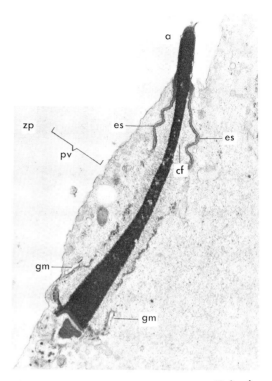

Fig. 9-3. Penetrating spermatozoon. Only the anterior end of the sperm head, *a*, is outside the egg. Invaginated regions of the fused cell membranes of the sperm and egg, *gm*, are shown at the base of the sperm nucleus. Note filamentous elements of the dispersing nucleus, *cf*; also see equatorial region, *es*; zona pellucida, *zp*; and perivitelline space, *pv*. (From Barros, C., and Franklin, L. E.: J. Cell Biol. **37:** C13, 1968.)

cal granules of the egg have been released, the second meiotic division of the ovum is resumed. This stage of the penetration process lasts for a relatively long time. The sperm head is then completely enveloped by veils of ooplasm, and fusion of the plasma membranes of the two gametes progresses so that the sperm head becomes completely incorporated into the ooplasm.

OVUM REACTION TO SPERM PENETRATION

The sperm head is incorporated into the ovum by a continuous elevation of the egg

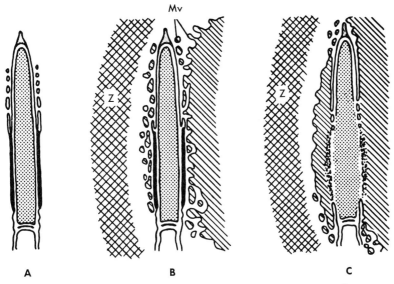

Fig. 9-4. Diagram showing stages in the fusion of spermatozoon and egg in the rat. **A,** Sagittal section of the sperm head near the end of the acrosome reaction. **B,** Sperm head in the perivitelline space becoming associated with microvilli, Mv. **C,** Fusion has occurred between the plasma membrane of the egg and the acrosomal and postnuclear-cap membranes of the spermatozoon. In these regions, the envelope of the sperm nucleus has disappeared. Zona pellucida, Z. (From Piko, L., and Tyler, A.: Proc. 5th Int. Cong. Anim. Reprod., Trento **2:**372-377, 1964.)

cortical cytoplasm. This process results in the formation of a conspicuous protuberance on the egg profile, which has been called an incorporation cone.[12] As the sperm completes its penetration, the incorporation cone is characterized by a linear area of condensed hyalin-like cytoplasm beneath the plasma membrane, and the overlying plasma membrane is smooth with a marked absence of microvilli. Studies on rat, hamster, and sea urchin eggs have shown that, following contract between the ovum and the sperm, there is a release and degradation of cortical granules (cortical reaction) and that contents of the granules combine with the plasma membrane of the ovum[15] (Fig. 9-5). These cortical granules are stained with special stains indicating the presence of polysaccharides. The outflow of the polysaccharide material from the ooplasm is essential for the chemical alteration of the zona pellucida (zona reac-tion) so that entry of additional spermatozoa is inhibited, thereby preventing polyspermy. In other species, the cortical granule reaction may be associated with the development of a jelly coat, the production of a hyalin layer, or merely the elevation of the fertilization membrane. Although a hyalin layer may be visualized in lower species, in the mammalian egg it has not been visualized in electron micrographs. Differences of the reaction occur between species—the result of a variation in the size as well as the number of cortical granules; it is likely that the differences are quantitative rather than qualitative. Following sperm penetration into rabbit eggs, there is a disappearance of these granules from the ooplasm. This is in contrast to the human where the persistence of some of the granules during fertilization indicates that there is only partial breakdown of the granules after sperm penetration rather

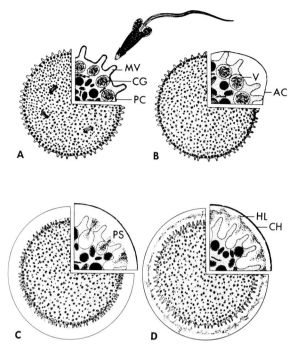

Fig. 9-5. Schematic representation of the events associated with the cortical reaction. **A,** Activation of the egg by the sperm: microvillus, *MV;* cortical granule, *CG;* and primary coat, *PC.* **B,** Lifting of primary (vitelline) coat to form the activation calyx, *AC,* and the union of the membrane of the cortical granules with that of the oolemma thereby forming vesicular structures, *V.* **C,** Release of the contents of the cortical granules within the perivitelline space, *PS.* **D,** Thick chorion, *CH,* and hyalin layer, *HL.* (From Anderson, E.: J. Cell Biol. **37**:514, 1968.)

than a total loss of granules as seen in other species.

The second polar body is formed immediately after fertilization. The chromosomes of the second polar body together with a small amount of ooplasm are extruded into the perivitelline space and this polar body usually lies close to the first polar body. In the rabbit, it has been shown that the chromosomes tend to clump approximately 12 hours after mating and then consist of a dense texture complete with a nuclear envelope. To date, only one human pronuclear egg has been studied by electron microscopy, and this egg contained three polar bodies. Presumably, the first polar body had undergone division and

the daughter cells were situated close together, showing a similar structure.

SPERM CHANGES FOLLOWING PENETRATION OF THE OVUM

Following penetration of the ovum plasma membrane, the sperm nucleus no longer has a membrane surrounding the anterior portion of the head. In the mouse, the posterior portion of nuclear chromatin is still surrounded by the postacrosomal cap with an underlying dilated space; this facilitates eventual separation of the cap from the nucleus.[12] Similarly, in the rat, the sperm nuclei lack membranes except where a portion of membrane persists where the tail was once inserted. When the postacrosomal cap is dissociated from the nucleus, small vesicles form in the adjacent ooplasm. As the chromatin material is fused, the nuclear chromatin becomes dispersed in the form of filaments of different lengths into the ooplasm. The entire nucleus becomes hydrated, beginning first in the periphery and later proceeding to the center. As hydration is completed, the nuclear mass is approximately four to five times the original size of the sperm nucleus; the chromatin material is filamentous and of low electron density. In the mouse, this hydration initially takes place in the postacrosomal cap region of the nucleus. In the development of the female pronucleus of the rabbit egg, a nuclear membrane is formed around each of the chromosomes that remain in the ooplasm following the release of the second polar body. Numerous pores are seen in the nuclear membrane at this stage. Subsequently there is fusion of the nuclear membrane of the chromosomes and, 14 hours after mating, an irregular small nucleus is formed. Shortly thereafter, the male and female pronuclei are in close apposition to each other, and it is not possible to distinguish between the male and the female pronucleus with electron microscope techniques. Protrusions of the nuclear membranes encircle portions of endoplasmic reticulum between the two pronuclei. In invertebrates, fusion of sperm and egg plasma membranes results in the perforation of the nuclear envelopes and the formation of an internuclear bridge.[16]

Only one human pronuclear egg has thus far been observed in a patient approximately 26 hours following coitus.[17] Both pronuclei were of approximately the same size, each containing a dense nucleolus; it was not possible to differentiate the male and female pronuclei because of the marked hydration of the chromatin material. Mitochondria, endoplasmic reticulum, and Golgi elements were present in the ooplasm around both nuclei. Numerous annulate lamellae and crystalloids were seen and it is thought that the latter represent the cytoplasmic yolk.

FATE OF THE EXTRANUCLEAR COMPONENTS OF SPERMATOZOA

Following penetration of the ooplasm, the sperm head is located within the incorporation cone. In those mammalian species studied by electron microscopy, the acrosomal material, the mid-piece, and the principal piece are also usually found in the ooplasm. Although these cellular components are incorporated into the ooplasm, the significance of their contribution to the future embryo or yolk components is not known.

Degenerative changes of the mid-piece and principal piece of the sperm tail have been observed in the human, mouse, and rat by electron microscopy.[12,17,18] In the mouse, degeneration occurs early in the mid-piece which undergoes fragmentation, distortion of the mitochondrial helix, and hydration of several of the helical components. In general, the implantation fossa remains with the caudal portion of the mid-piece. Degeneration of the fibers of the sperm tail begins relatively early; in the rat, however, the sperm tail may persist up to the 8-cell stage of the embryo and possibly even later. Following penetration, the inner fibers degenerate before the outer coarse fibers which retain their appearance longer. In the human pronuclear egg, the dense outer fibers and axial filament complex were easily recognized and were relatively close to one of the pronuclei.

The acrosomal material and postacrosomal cap become separated from the nucleus soon after fusion of the gamete membranes. In the mouse, as separation occurs, vesicle formation in the acrosomal area takes place, presumably resulting from the interaction between the surrounding ooplasm and the acrosome. At a later stage, the remnant of the postacrosomal cap assumes an irregular V-shaped configuration and may be seen lying free in the ooplasm.

No remnants of the acrosomal region or postacrosomal cap were noted in the serially sectioned human pronuclear egg.

REFERENCES

1. Lillie, F.: The mechanism of fertilization, Science 38:524, 1913.
2. Tyler, A.: Some immunobiological experiments on fertilization and early development in sea urchins, Exp. Cell Res. 7(supp.):183, 1959.
3. Tyler, A.: The manipulation of macromolecular substances during fertilization and early development of animal eggs, Amer. Zool. 3: 109, 1963.
4. Runnstrom, J., Tiselius, A., and Vasseur, E.: Zur kenntnis der gamonwirkungen bei Psammechinus miliaris und Echino cardium cordatum, Ark. Kemi. Min. Och. Geol. 15a:1-18, 1942.
5. Bishop, D. W., and Tyler, A.: Fertilizing of mammalian eggs, J. Exp. Zool. 132:575, 1956.
6. Schwartz, R., Brooks, W., and Zinsser, H. H.: Evidence of chemotaxis as a factor in sperm motility, Fertil. Steril. 9:300, 1958.
7. Bateman, N.: Selective fertilization at the T-locus of the mouse, Genet. Res. 1:226, 1960.
8. Braden, A. W. H.: Genetic influences on the morphology and function of the gametes, J. Cell. Comp. Physiol. 56(supp. 1):17, 1960.
9. Tyler, A.: Extraction of an egg membrane-lysin from sperm of the giant keyhole limpet (Megathura crenulata), Proc. Nat. Acad. Sci. 25:317, 1939.
10. Barros, C., Bedford, J. M., Franklin, L. E., and Austin, C. R.: Membrane vesiculation as a feature of the mammalian acrosome reaction, J. Cell Biol. 34:C1, 1967.
11. Bedford, J. M.: Ultrastructural changes in the sperm head during fertilization in the rabbit, Amer. J. Anat. 123:329, 1968.
12. Stefanini, M., Oura, C., and Zamboni, L.: Ultrastructure of fertilization in the mouse. II. Penetration of sperm into the ovum, J. Submicr. Cytol. 1:1, 1969.
13. Piko, L., and Tyler, A.: Fine structural studies of sperm penetration in the rat, Proc. 5th Int. Cong. Anim. Reprod., Trento 2:372-377, 1964.
14. Barros, C., and Franklin, L. E.: Behavior of the gamete membranes during sperm entry into the mammalian egg, J. Cell Biol. 37:C13, 1968.
15. Anderson, E.: Oocyte differentiation in the sea urchin, Arbacia punctulata, with particular reference to the origin of cortical granules and their participation in the cortical reaction, J. Cell Biol. 37:514, 1968.
16. Longo, F. J., and Anderson, E.: The fine structure of pronuclear development and fusion in the sea urchin, Arbacia punctulata, J. Cell Biol. 39:339, 1968.
17. Zamboni, L., Mishell, D. R., Jr., Bell, J. H., and Baca, M.: Fine structure of the human ovum in the pronuclear stage, J. Cell Biol. 30:579, 1966.
18. Szollosi, D.: The fate of sperm middle-piece mitochondria in the rat egg, J. Exp. Zool. 159:367, 1965.

ADDITIONAL READINGS

Austin, C. R.: Fertilization, Englewood Cliffs, N. J., 1965, Prentice-Hall, Inc.
Austin, C. R.: Ultrastructure of fertilization, New York, 1968, Holt, Rinehart & Winston, Inc.

CHAPTER 10

Implantation and early embryogenesis

IMPLANTATION

During its migration from the fallopian tube to the uterine cavity, the fertilized ovum undergoes a series of cellular divisions. Implantation occurs approximately 6 or 7 days after fertilization when the single ovum has divided to form approximately 200 cells. Once the developing zygote reaches the uterine wall, an important and incompletely understood synchronization of development is necessary to permit implantation. Noyes et al.[1] have demonstrated in rats and mice that an egg will not survive if transplanted into a uterus unless the postcoital ages of the egg and uterus are similar; if the recipient uterus is 24 hours or more ahead of the transplanted egg, the egg will not survive. Thus preparation of the endometrium is of major importance. At this time, the corpus luteum is secreting large quantities of progesterone, which alter the endometrium. Estrogens administered at this stage will hasten tubal transport and prevent implantation in laboratory animals. A variety of antiprogestogens also will prevent implantation.[2] The somewhat flattened shape of the uterus, which results in primarily anterior and posterior walls, makes implantation most likely on one of these two surfaces.[3] Although the blastocyst survives in a predominantly anaerobic state prior to implantation, the increasing cell numbers and limited surface area necessitate establishing a blood circulation. By active invasion, the blastocyst burrows down into the endometrium; after 7½ days the endometrial epithelium has proliferated over it. A large portion of the cellular mass has become differentiated into trophoblastic cells at this stage—principally syncytiotrophoblastic cells. (See Fig. 10-6.) These cells all divide rapidly in the rich environment of the endometrium, with its lacunae filled with blood and its ready gas exchange, to form the early placenta. As large masses of syncytiotrophoblast form, spaces appear that later become the intravillous spaces. Aggregations and columns of syncytiotrophoblast form and organize with central connective tissue to become the villi. The greatest growth rate is on the side toward the endometrium and toward the maternal circulation. The endometrial epithelium covering the trophoblast prevents its contact with its opposite uterine wall; thus the placenta develops on only one side.

HUMAN CHORIONIC GONADOTROPIN (HCG)
Production

As nidation is occurring and the number of trophoblastic cells increases rapidly, HCG concentrations increase in the blood proportionately.[4,5] Fig. 10-1 shows the rate of increase in HCG concentrations of six women in whom the time of conception was known. Prior to the time of the first expected missed menses, HCG concentrations became elevated and in all six women increased in a linear fashion* (doubling time = 2.7 days).

---

*Elaboration of a placental gonadotropin is not common in nature; only higher primates appear to secrete such a hormone. The only other animal known to possess a pregnancy gonadotropin is the mare; the endometrial cups of the pregnant mare (horse, zebra) elaborate pregnant mare serum gonadotropin.

131

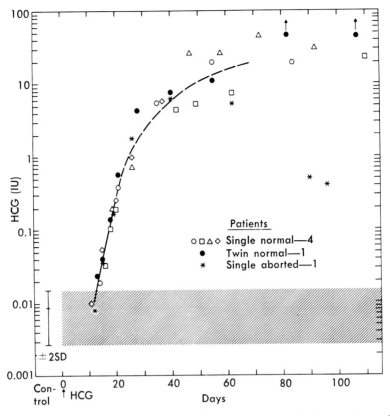

Fig. 10-1. Serum HCG concentrations (IU/ml) in six women with known time of ovulation. Follicular growth was induced with human menopausal gonadotropin (HMG), and ovulation induced with a single dose of human chorionic gonadotropin (HCG) given on day zero. The 95% limits of LH activity are indicated by the shaded area. The rise of HCG pictured is derived from HCG secretion by the rapidly proliferating trophoblastic cells and occurred before the next expected menses. Note that data from all six women cluster on the same line of HCG increase until approximately day 30. (From Marshall, J. R., Hammond, C. B., Ross, G. T., Jacobson, A., Rayford, P., and Odell, W. D.: Obstet. Gynec. **32:**760, 1968.)

As the fetal-placental unit develops, further individual variations occur but mean HCG concentrations progressively continue to increase. Fig. 10-2 shows the changes in blood HCG concentration as determined throughout pregnancy.

Actions

The function of HCG is not entirely clear. As has been stated, the placentas of most animal species do not elaborate a gonadotropin. HCG actions in bioassays give responses indistinguishable from pituitary LH. HCG in large amounts has been shown to prolong the life-span of the corpus luteum in monkeys[6] and humans.[7] Ovariectomy performed after the first month or two of pregnancy does not appear to terminate gestation.[8] Thus HCG is presumed to be involved in the transition from ovarian steroid hormone production to placental steroid production that is required for ni-

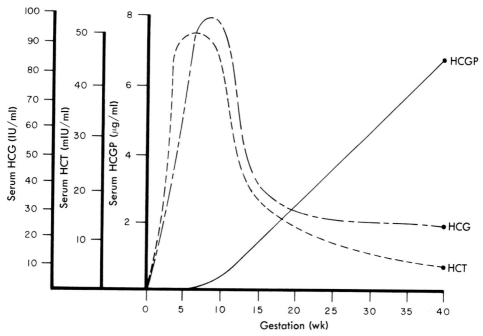

Fig. 10-2. Schematic presentation of changes in serum human chorionic gonadotropin (HCG), human chorionic growth hormone prolactin (HCGP), and human chorionic thyrotropin (HCT). (Based on data from Mishell et al.,[5] Grumbach et al.,[12] and Hennen et al.[16])

dation and early gestation. In many animals not producing placental gonadotropins, ovariectomy early in pregnancy results in abortion. However, Yoshimi et al.[9] have recently shown that increasing HCG concentrations do not correlate with corpus luteum function. Although most reproductive physiologists believe that HCG acts in this important function of bridging the transition from ovarian to placental steroid function, details remain obscure. (See Fig. 10-3.)

The detection of HCG in blood or urine has been used for many years to diagnose pregnancy or gonadotropin-producing tumors. For discussion of the production of gonadotropins by tumors see the review of Odell et al.[10]

HUMAN CHORIONIC GROWTH HORMONE–PROLACTIN (HCGP)

The human placenta also elaborates a polypeptide hormone that is chemically and immunologically similiar to human pituitary growth hormone and that has been reported to have some prolactin and growth hormone–like properties. Josimovich and Brande[11] isolated and purified this material, and Grumbach et al.[12] and Josimovich and Mintz[13] have recently reviewed its biological properties.

Production and secretion

In contrast to HCG, HCGP (human chorionic gonadotropin from placenta) is not produced in large amounts early in pregnancy. Fig. 10-2 diagrams the rise in serum HCGP during pregnancy. Only a tiny fraction of the HCGP produced each day is excreted in the urine; the studies of Grumbach et al.[12] indicate that less than 2% is excreted. These workers have also shown that the disappearance of HCGP from blood after delivery follows a biphasic curve; the early phase has a half-time of dis-

133

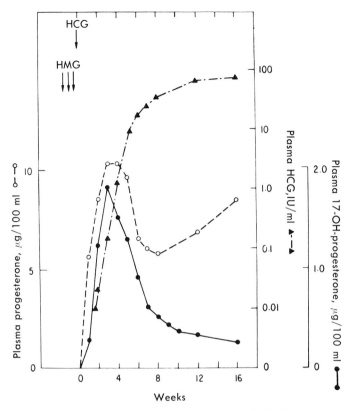

Fig. 10-3. Plasma concentrations of progesterone o- -o, 17-hydroxyprogesterone o—o, and HCG ▲- -▲ from conception to 16 weeks of gestation. Note that HCG concentrations rise progressively for about 8 weeks, then begin to plateau, while 17-hydroxyprogesterone, secreted by the ovary but not the placenta, rises for 3 weeks, then falls. Progesterone concentrations rise, fall, then rise again as placental formation adds to a changing ovarian secretion. The placenta is unable to 17-hydroxylate progesterone; therefore 17-hydroxyprogesterone concentrations represent ovarian secretory activity. Ovulation was induced in this woman by treatment with human menopausal gonadotropin (HMG) and HCG. (From Yoshimi, T., Strott, C. A., Marshall, P. R., and Lipsett, M. B.: J. Clin. Endocr. **29:**225, 1969.)

appearance of 13 minutes, and the later phase a half-time of 48 minutes.

Properties

Highly purified HCGP has now been prepared in a number of laboratories. Studies of possible metabolic effects are conflicting. Grumbach et al.[12] have reported that doses of 100 to 200 mg/day administered to growth hormone–deficient dwarfs produced a significant nitrogen retention, an increased insulin secretion in response to glucose loading, and a slowing of the clearance rate of glucose from blood. In contrast, Josimovich and Mintz[13] failed to find such effects on carbohydrate metabolism studied under similar circumstances. Shultz and Blizzard[14] failed to find significant nitrogen retention when growth hormone–deficient dwarfs were treated. Assuming the observations of Grumbach are correct, however, similar effects may be produced by 1 or 2 mg of pituitary growth hormone. Thus HCGP possesses *at most* about 1% of the growth hormone–like activity of pituitary growth hormone. However, it is secreted in gram amounts each day; (blood concentrations reach 6 or more $\mu g/ml$ of serum) and these concentrations are sufficient to achieve the effects reported. Growth hormone concentrations, in contrast, usually range from 0.001 to 0.05 $\mu g/ml$. Pregnancy is associated with striking alterations in carbohydrate metabolism. It is attractive to attribute these alterations to the high blood concentrations of HCGP. Further studies are required before this hypothesis can be fully accepted.

HUMAN CHORIONIC THYROTROPIN (HCT)

Approximately 7% of patients with metastatic trophoblastic disease (choriocarcinoma, etc.) have thyrotoxicosis. Odell et al.[10,15] reported that this syndrome is caused by the tumor elaboration of a thyrotropin-like material that has biochemical and biological properties similar to pituitary TSH, but it can be distinguished from pituitary TSH by immunological means. Hennen et al.[16] extracted normal placentas and concentrated and purified this thyrotropin-like material. The material was purified by the same techniques used to purify human pituitary TSH. However, it possessed about 5% of the biological potency of pituitary TSH and it reacted poorly with antisera directed against human TSH, to the extent that 3000 times more HCT by weight was required to produce a given reaction in the human TSH radioimmunoassay. Hennen et al.[16] in 1969 reported the changes of blood HCT during the course of pregnancy. These are shown in Fig. 10-2. Note that both HCT and HCGP are secreted in large amounts, but both have only a tiny fraction of the biological activity of pituitary trophic hormones. HCG, by contrast, is a potent gonadotropin on a weight basis—probably biologically equal to pituitary LH.

PRODUCTION OF STEROID HORMONES[8,17-19]

The steroidogenic sequence of biochemical reactions has been described in Chapters 5 and 6. The existence of these synthetic steps within the ovary has been well documented; ovarian tissue converts acetate and cholesterol to progesterone, estradiol, and estrone. In contrast, placental tissue does not appear capable of converting cholesterol or acetate to estrogens, nor of converting progesterone to estrogens. During pregnancy, however, progesterone, estradiol, estrone, and estriol blood concentrations increase markedly, indicating an increased production of these steroids. Diczfalusy[17] and Simmer[8] have reviewed many aspects of placental steroid production and the interested reader is referred to these publications for details and additional references. Although the isolated perfused placenta is unable to convert precursor cholesterol or progesterone to estrogens, it possesses great enzymatic activity capable of converting C-19 steroids (androstenedione, testosterone, dehydroepiandrosterone) to estrogens. Diczfalusy suggested, therefore, that placental estrogen synthesis occurs principally by aromatization of C-19 steroid precursors reaching the placenta via the fetal or maternal circulation. In support of this concept, Diczfalusy et al. observed that when C-19 steroids were infused into the isolated, perfused placenta, over 70% were converted to phenolic material (mostly estrogens). Bolte et al.,[18] in a series of studies, demonstrated that dehydroepiandrosterone (a C-19 steroid secreted in large amounts as the *sulfate* from fetal sources or circulating within the fetoplacental unit) is converted into estrogens to a far greater extent than is the dehydroepiandrosterone sulfate present in the maternal circulation. Furthermore, much more dehydroepiandrosterone sulfate from the fetoplacental circulation is converted into urinary estriol than is dehydroepiandrosterone sulfate from the maternal circulation. These observations

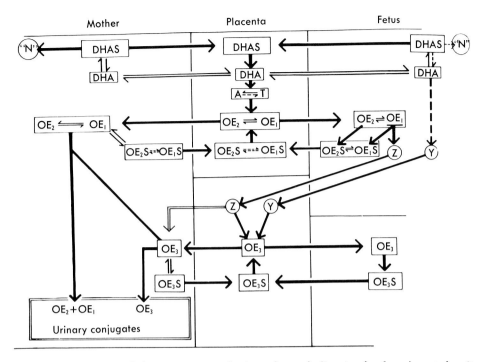

Fig. 10-4. Concept of the estrogen synthesis and metabolism in the fetoplacental unit. Arrows with dotted lines indicate unproved reactions, DHA indicates dehydroepiandrosterone, and DHAS its sulfate. N indicates various neutral metabolites of DHAS; A is androstenedione; T is testosterone; OE_1, OE_2, and OE_3 are estrone, 17β-estradiol, and estriol; and OE_1S, OE_2S, and OE_3S their three sulfates. Z stands for a 16-hydroxylated phenolic intermediate formed by the fetus from placental estrone; Y is a 16-hydroxylated neutral metabolite formed from DHAS circulating in the fetus. (From Diczfalusy, E.: Fed. Proc. **23:**791, 1964, and constructed according to Bolte, E. S., Mancuso, G., Eriksson, N., Wigrist, N., and Diczfalusy, E.: Acta Endocr. **45:**567, 1964.)

have led Bolte et al.[18] to construct the scheme of steroid biosynthesis by the fetoplacental unit pictured in Fig. 10-4. According to this scheme, the placenta carries out little or no estrogen synthesis *de novo.* Fetal and maternal dehydroepiandrosterone (DHA) serve as principal estrogen precursors, but the relative contributions differ as discussed above. In all probability, the fetal adrenal gland is the major source of fetal dehydroepiandrosterone sulfate. Within the placenta, dehydroepiandrosterone sulfate is converted to dehydroepiandrosterone, then to androstenedione and testosterone. The latter undergoes "A" ring aromatization to estrone and estradiol and diffuses back to fetal and maternal circulations. Further metabolism occurs in maternal and fetal circulation; thus urinary conjugates of estrone, estradiol, and estriol are excreted. This scheme explains why estrogen production is low (relative to normal pregnancy) in women with trophoblastic neoplasms and in women with anencephalic monsters (who may lack normal adrenal function, with ACTH deficiency) but is normal in mothers with adrenal insufficiency (see reviews listed in reference 18).

Progesterone production is markedly increased during pregnancy in the absence

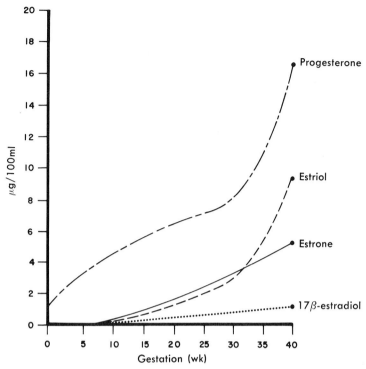

Fig. 10-5. Schematic presentation of the changes in blood progesterone, estriol, estrone, and 17β-estradiol seen throughout pregnancy. (Based on data from Kaiser[3] and Simmer.[8])

of maternal ovaries, adrenals, or absence of the fetus. The placenta is capable of synthesizing progesterone from acetate or cholesterol. In addition, however, fetal and maternal precursors (pregnenolone and 17-hydroxyprogesterone) are actively converted to progesterone. Fetal contributions, in contrast to the estrogen production scheme, appear to be small; interruption of the fetoplacental circulatory connections diminishes excretion of urinary pregnanediol, the urinary excretory product of progesterone (Fig. 10-5).

OTHER PHYSIOLOGICAL ALTERATIONS

The preceding sections of Chapter 10 have described the fetoplacental production of steroid and polypeptide hormones; the actions of these hormones have largely been discussed in earlier chapters of the text.

Most of the striking alterations in maternal physiology occur during later portions of pregnancy. The absence of menses, the suppression of subsequent ovulation caused by the prolonged life of the corpus luteum and estrogen-progestogen production, the increasing production of HCG, and resultant maternal effects of these altered hormone productions account for the observed early alterations in maternal physiology. Such alterations occurring later in pregnancy (after two months) are extremely complex and will not be discussed herein. Hytten and Thomson[20] have recently reviewed such maternal changes as alterations in blood volume and composition, venous pressure, cardiac output, oxygen consumption, respiration, renal function, and gastrointestinal function. Changes in these parameters occur at greater than 2 months

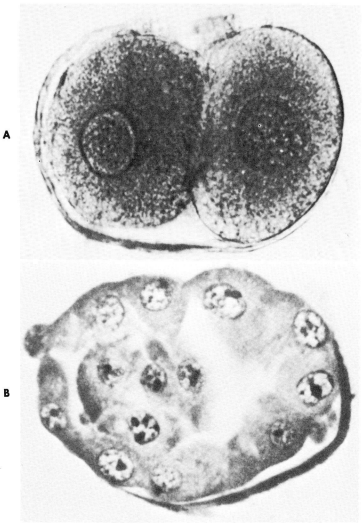

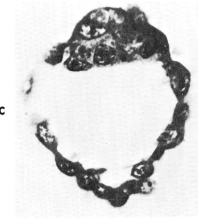

Fig. 10-6. A, A 2-cell human ovum recovered from fallopian tubes. Its age was estimated to be about 36 hours after conception. Note the polar bodies at the lower margin and at the upper margin of the cleavage plane. (×500.) B, A 58-cell human blastula recovered from the uterine cavity within 4 days of conception. The polar body is visible on left. (×600.) C, A 107-cell human blastula recovered from the uterine cavity. Note the larger size and less differentiated nature of the 8 formative cells of the germ disc. (×600.)

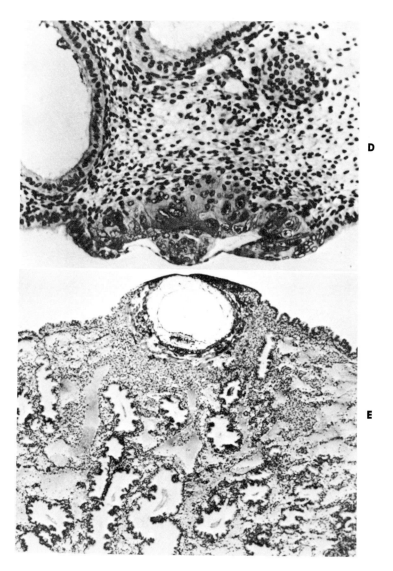

Fig. 10-6, cont'd. D, Section through the middle of a blastocyst implanted within the endometrium. The age of the conceptus was estimated to be 7 days. The endometrium is shown in the top three fourths of this section, the blastocyst at the bottom. The bilaminar nature of the serum disc is evident. The early primordium of the amniotic cavity appears as a cleft between it and the cytotrophoblast. Note large multinucleated masses of syncytiotrophoblast growing into the edematous endometrial stroma. (×400.) **E,** Human conceptus, estimated 12 days of age. The ovum is shallowly implanted, with the overlying endometrium present, but thin, atrophic or definitely necrotic. Several large vascular sinusoids supplying the trophoblast with blood are seen near the ovum. The glands of the endometrium are in marked secretory activity. (×60.) (**A** to **C** from Hertig, A. T., Rock, J., Adams, E. C., and Mulligan, W. J.: J. Contrib. Embryol. **35:**199, 1954; **D** and **E** from Hertig, A. T., and Rock, J.: J. Contrib. Embryol. **31:**65, 1945.)

gestation, but not earlier, and the interested reader is referred to this excellent review. Certainly it is important to emphasize, as those authors have, that pregnancy cannot be regarded as only a process of fetal growth superimposed on the ordinary metabolism of the mother. In the future, more detailed studies of the first 2 to 8 weeks of gestation may lead to an understanding of subtle physiological changes presently unknown. However, during the first 4 to 6 weeks of pregnancy, the process of fetal growth may be merely superimposed on the metabolism of the mother *only* modified by increased estrogen, progestogen, HCT, and HCG production.

Fig. 10-6, *A* to *E,* taken from the studies of Hertig et al.[21] and of Hertig and Rock,[22,23] shows sequential development from a two-cell human embryo to the early implanted specimen.

REFERENCES

1. Noyes, R. W., Dickmann, Z., Doyle, L. L., and Gates, A. H.: Ovum transfers, synchronous and asynchronous, in the study of implantation. In Enders, A. C., editor: Delayed implantation, Chicago, 1963, University of Chicago Press.
2. Pincus, G.: Hormonal steroids in preimplantation stages. In Wolstenholme, G. E. W., editor: Preimplantation stages of pregnancy, Boston, 1965, Little, Brown & Co.
3. Kaiser, I. H.: Maternal physiology. In Danforth, D. N., editor: Textbook of obstetrics and gynecology, New York, 1966, Harper & Row, publishers.
4. Marshall, J. R., Hammond, C. B., Ross, G. T., Jacobson, A., Rayford, P., and Odell, W. D.: Plasma and urinary chorionic gonadotrophin during early human pregnancy, Obstet. Gynec. 32:760, 1968.
5. Mishell, D. R., Jr., Wide, L., and Gemzell, C.: Immunologic determination of human chorionic gonadotropin in serum, J. Clin. Endocr. 23:125, 1969.
6. Hisaw, F. L.: The placental gonadotrophin and luteal function in monkeys (Macaca mulatta), Yale J. Biol. Med. 17:119, Oct., 1944.
7. Brown, W. E., and Bradbury, J. T.: A study of the physiologic action of human chorionic gonadotropin, Amer. J. Obstet. Gynec. 53:749, 1947.
8. Simmer, H.: Placental hormones. In Assali, N. S., editor: Biology of gestation, vol. 1, New York, 1968, Academic Press, Inc.
9. Yoshimi, T., Strott, C. A., Marshall, J. R., and Lipsett, M. B.: Corpus luteum function in early pregnancy, J. Clin. Endocr. 29:225, 1969.
10. Odell, W. D., Hertz, R., Lipsett, M. B., Ross, G. T., and Hammond, C. B.: Endocrine aspects of trophoblastic neoplasms, Clin. Obstet. Gynec. 10:290, 1967.
11. Josimovich, J. B., and Brande, B. L. C.: Chemical properties and biological effects of human placental lactogen (HPL), Trans. N. Y. Acad. Sci. 27:161, 1964.
12. Grumbach, M. M., Kaplan, S. L., Sciarra, J. J., and Burr, I. M.: Chorionic growth hormone—prolactin (CGP): secretion, disposition, biologic activity in man, and postulated function as the growth hormone of the second half of pregnancy, Ann. N. Y. Acad. Sci. 148:501, 1968.
13. Josimovich, J. B., and Mintz, D. H.: Biological and immunological studies on human placental lactogen, Ann. N. Y. Acad. Sci. 148:488, 1968.
14. Shultz, R. B., and Blizzard, R. M.: A comparison of human placental lactogen (HPL) and human growth hormone (HGH) in hypopituitary patients, J. Clin. Endocr. 26:921, 1966.
15. Odell, W. D., Bates, R. W., Rivlin, R. S., Lipsett, M. B., and Hertz, R.: Increased thyroid function without clinical hyperthyroidism in patients with choriocarcinoma, J. Clin. Endocr. 23:658, 1963.
16. Hennen, G., Pierce, J. G., and Freychet, P.: Human chorionic thyrotropin: further characterization and study of its secretion during pregnancy, J. Clin. Endocr. 29:581, 1969.
17. Diczfalusy, E.: Endocrine functions of the human placental unit, Fed. Proc. 23:791, 1964.
18. Bolte, E. S., Mancuso, G., Eriksson, N., Wigrist, N., and Diczfalusy, E.: Studies on the aromatization of neutral steroids in pregnant women, Acta Endocr. 45:576, 1964.
19. Cassmer, O.: Hormone production of the isolated human placenta: studies on the role of the foetus in the endocrine function of the placenta, Acta Endocr. 32(supp. 45):1, 1959.
20. Hytten, F. E., and Thomson, A. M.: Maternal physiological adjustments. In Assali, N. S., editor: Biology of gestation, vol. 1, New York, 1968, Academic Press, Inc.
21. Hertig, A. T., Rock, J., Adams, E. C., and Mulligan, W. J.: On the preimplantation stages of the human ovum: a description of

four normal and four abnormal specimens ranging from the second to the fifth day of development, J. Contrib. Embryol. **35**:199, 1954.

22. Hertig, A. T., and Rock, J.: Two human ova of the pre-villous stage, having a develop-mental age of about seven and nine days respectively, J. Contrib. Embryol. **31**:65, 1945.

23. Hertig, A. T., and Rock, J.: Two human ova of the pre-villous stage having an ovulation age of about eleven and twelve days respectively, J. Contrib. Embryol. **29**:127, 1941.

CHAPTER 11

Prevention of fertility

This text was not intended to discuss clinical pathophysiology, and we have therefore omitted reference or discussion of infertility, hypogonadism, amenorrhea, problems of intersex, and many other areas of major importance to clinical endocrinologists. In this sense a chapter on contraception is not entirely appropriate. However, inasmuch as this is presently an area of intense research activity, an area of major interest to many world governments, and a subject of which careful consideration brings together the majority of the information presented in preceding chapters of this text, we have elected to include a brief discussion.

Figs. 11-1 and 11-2 present in schematic form the interrelations between all portions of the endocrine and reproductive organs. Details have been presented and form the background required for interpretation. These interrelations are complex and it appears that full action and integration of all facets of this system must occur to result in the prime function, presentation of a viable ovum to sperm under conditions permitting conception and subsequent growth and development. In theory, interference at almost any phase of this sequence of physiological events could prevent fertility.

Many preventive aspects are related to each of the steps listed in the accompanying outlines. For example, the process of sperm penetration into and fertilization of the ovum is complex and involves a number of sequential steps. The sum of events dissected and considered in detail is as complex as all our discussions of the processes of reproduction. Interference with any phase of this would obviously have the end result of preventing conception. Consideration of the entire reproductive sequence in such detail would require a book many times thicker than this. For some of the details, the interested reader is referred to the outstanding review by Pincus.[1]

Consideration of possible means of preventing fertility in women*

I. *Interference with sperm action*
   A. Prevention of sperm entrance to vagina
   B. Prevention of sperm entrance to uterus
   C. Prevention of sperm entrance to fallopian tubes
   D. Creation of hostile environment to sperm in vagina, uterus, or tubes
   E. Prevention of sperm penetration of ovum by action on sperm

II. *Interference with ovum action*
   A. Prevention of ova release from ovary
   B. Prevention of ova entrance to fallopian tube
   C. Creation of hostile environment for ova in fallopian tubes
   D. Prevention of sperm penetration of ovum by action on ova

III. *Prevention of survival of fertilized ova*
   A. Prevention of fertilized ova from undergoing mitosis
   B. Prevention of migration along fallopian tube
   C. Prevention of nidation of blastocyst in uterine wall
   D. Destruction of embryo after nidation in uterine wall

IV. *Interference with ovarian function at ovarian level*

---

*Not listed is surgical removal of any of the components (e.g., uterus, fallopian tubes, ovaries).

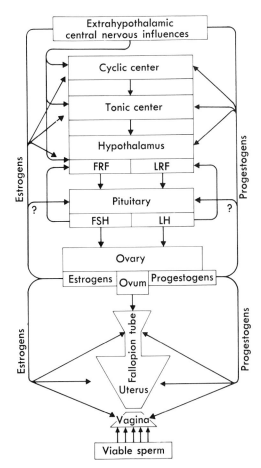

Fig. 11-1. Schematic presentation of interrelations between various portions of the reproductive system in women. Arrows simply indicate an action on that facet of the system. The action may be either stimulatory or suppressive; details have been discussed in earlier chapters.

A. Prevention of initiation of follicle growth (no response to early FSH rise)
B. Prevention of response to ovulatory LH-FSH peak
C. Prevention of maturation of follicle or maturation of ova (e.g., inhibition of meiotic phases, polar body formation)
D. Prevention of corpus luteum formation
E. Prevention of ovarian estrogen secretion
F. Prevention of ovarian progestogen secretion
G. Prevention of the prolonged life of the corpus luteum associated with early pregnancy
V. *Interference with pituitary function*
   A. Prevention of FSH and/or LH secretion at a pituitary level
   B. Prevention of action of LRF or FRF on pituitary
   C. Prevention of secretion of FRF or LRF
   D. Prevention of estrogen or progestogen action on tonic center

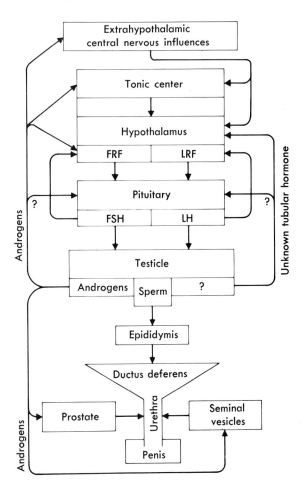

Fig. 11-2. Schematic presentation of interrelations between various portions of the reproductive system in men.

E. Prevention of estrogen or progestogen action on cyclic center

F. Abolishment of extrahypothalamic central nervous factors required for normal reproductive hypothalamic function

G. ? Prevention of FSH or LH action on hypothalamus, tonic center, or cyclic center

Consideration of possible means of preventing fertility in men[*]

I. *Interference with sperm survival*
   A. Prevention of maturation process in epididymis
   B. Prevention of function of seminal vesicle
      1. Prevention of androgen action on seminal vesicle
      2. Prevention of formation of seminal vesicle secretion
      3. Prevention of seminal vesicle secretion from entering urethra
   C. Prevention of function of prostate
      1. Prevention of androgen action on prostate
      2. Prevention of formation of prostatic secretion
      3. Prevention of prostatic secretion from entering urethra
   D. Creation of hostile environment to sperm in vas deferens or urethra

II. *Interference with testicular function at testicular level*
   A. Prevention of action of LH on interstitial cells
   B. Prevention of androgen action on spermatic tublues
   C. Prevention of action of FSH on spermatic tubules
   D. Prevention of spermatogenesis

III. *Interference with pituitary function*
   A. Prevention of FSH or LH secretion at a pituitary level
   B. Prevention of action of LRF or FRF on pituitary
   C. Prevention of secretion of FRF or LRF
   D. Prevention of androgen action on tonic center
   E. Prevention of action of unknown spermatic tubule hormone on tonic center
   F. Abolishment of extrahypothalamic central nervous factors required for normal reproductive function
   G. ? Prevention of FSH or LH action on hypothalamus, tonic center, or cyclic center

[*]Not listed are surgical interventions removing source of sperm such as castration or preventing egress of sperm such as vasectomy.

At the present time, some of the most widely used means of contraception include (1) oral contraceptives administered to women, (2) intrauterine devices, and (3) various forms of mechanical devices for controlling sperm access to the ovum (condom, diaphragm). Effective means of controlling fertility in men using orally administered medications have not been commonly used.[1] Most available medications appear to be associated with side effects (progestogens, estrogens). A notable exception is androgen treatment, which on long-term administration appears to suppress circulating gonadotropin and produce oligospermia.[2,3] Clinical studies using such treatment to control fertility of men appear not to have been performed to date. We shall discuss the hormonal effects of oral contraceptives, and some aspects of the intrauterine devices. Mechanical devices for preventing sperm-ovum union represent fairly obvious physiological alterations and will not be discussed.

ORAL CONTRACEPTIVES

Three types of oral contraceptives are presently in common use.

1. Combined type. Estrogen and progestogen are administered together in the same dosage each day usually for 20 days. Drugs are then discontinued for 5 days, readministered for 20 days, etc.

2. Sequential type. Estrogen is administered alone for 15 days followed by estrogen plus progestogen for 5 days.

3. Progestogen administered alone. Dosage may be either continuous or intermittent.

The mechanisms of contraception of each of these agents are complex and not all aspects are understood. The best understood are the combined type.[4,5] The effect of this type of contraceptive on serum LH and FSH is presented in Fig. 11-3. Also shown for comparison are the fluctuations in LH and FSH observed during a normal menstrual cycle. Both LH and FSH are sup-

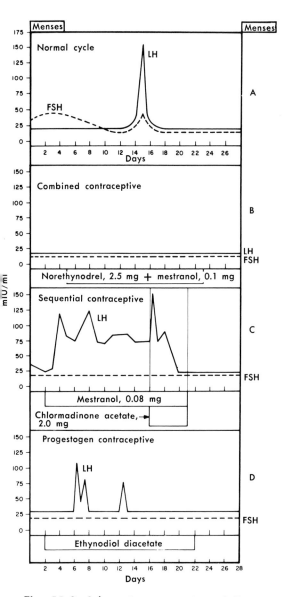

Fig. 11-3. Schematic presentation of fluctuations in LH and FSH during a normal menstrual cycle, **A**; and during treatment with a "combined type" oral contraceptive, **B**, a "sequential type" oral contraceptive, **C**, and a progestogen, **D**. (Based on data from Ross et al.,[4] Swerdloff and Odell,[5] Mishell and Odell,[6] and Odell et al.[7])

pressed by this combination treatment, and levels are about the same throughout the cycle as those observed during the luteal phase of the normal cycle. There is no early rise in FSH, and no midcycle LH-FSH peak. The mechanism of action of this contraceptive is the abolition of both the small FSH rise initiating follicular growth and the ovulatory LH-FSH surge. Thus follicular growth is not initiated and ovulation does not occur.

The effects of the sequential type of contraceptive are also shown in Fig. 11-3. The estrogen treatment appears to stimulate LH (but not FSH) secretion; blood concentrations increase repeatedly in unusual multiple peaks.[5] When the progestogen is added, another LH peak is usually produced, unless a peak has already occurred on the last day or two preceding. The mechanism of action of this type of contraception is not known for certain. It does abolish ovulation, possibly by abolishing the early FSH rise and resultant initiation of follicle growth.

Fig. 11-3 also depicts schematically the fluctuations of LH and FSH during treatment with a progestogen.[6] Note that frequently multiple bazaar LH fluctuations were noted, but that no changes in FSH were observed. In general, progressive increase in this progestogen dosage was associated with progressively fewer LH peaks, and on the highest dose studied many women had no LH peaks. In most instances ovulation continued on low-dose progestogen treatment and cylic uterine bleeding is also observed. Thus this contraceptive may be taken continuously with few or no side effects. Mechanisms of contraception remain obscure. Alterations in cervical mucus and inhibition of sperm penetration may result.

INTRAUTERINE DEVICES

Intrauterine devices (IUD) were introduced by a German physician, Von Grafenberg, in the early 1900s. His silver and steel devices fell into disrepute because of inability to control severe side effects: uterine perforation and peritoneal infections. About two decades ago, less reactive plastic devices were introduced, and they were found to have a high rate of effectiveness (96%) and minimal side effects.

IUDs are foreign bodies in the intrauterine cavity, and as such produce a characteristic morphological and biochemical response. In every species thus far studied, including humans, migration of increased quantities of polymorphonuclear leukocytes and other inflammatory cells has been noted in endometrial sections taken from uteri containing the IUD.[8] Particularly when the endometrial tissues are soft, the intrauterine device may produce a U-shaped depression in the superficial endometrium, in which ulcerations may not be seen. In other patients microscopic ulcerations of the superficial epithelium are noted underlying the areas of contact of the intrauterine device, with the resultant movement of neutrophils into this area. Migration of the neutrophils into the uterine cavity and subsequent cytolysis release the intracellular components of the increased number of leukocytes. It is likely that these substances, which are not normally present, are responsible for the antifertility effect. The inflammatory response to the foreign body is a sterile response; cultures usually reveal no bacterial growth except during a transient bacterial infection upon insertion of the IUD through the cervical canal.

The mode of action of the intrauterine devices is still not fully known.[10] Early workers felt that the device acted as an abortifacient and suggested that it might alter the endometrium to disturb implantation. Other investigators[9] have shown that tubal motility is increased while the device is in place, suggesting that the unfertilized ova may be rapidly expelled prematurely into the uterine or vaginal cavities before fertilization can take place. It is known that sperm may be found at the usual site of fertilization in the ampulla of the fallopian tube, indicating that sperm migration is not impaired. A more recent hypothesis for the mode of action of the intrauterine device is that it produces both the foreign body reaction described and an increased amount of uterine fluid. The foreign body reaction is nonspecific in action, and effective fertility control is only one of many end results; these may also include abnormal uterine bleeding, and myometrial and tubal contractions that result in expulsion of the device and in asynchronous maturation of the endometrial tissues.[11]

In spite of this rather unfavorable presentation of the IUD, they have gained widespread use for two reasons: (1) they are inexpensive; (2) they require no continued effort or planned program such as is necessary with use of oral contraceptives.

In summary, the rapidly accumulating and vast knowledge concerning reproduction has resulted in a few effective methods of contraception. However, none represents the ideal contraceptive with the rapidly increasing population, increasing numbers of underfed, undereducated, and suppressed peoples in existence. Application of the principles presented in this text has led to sufficient understanding so that one day a foolproof, safe, and inexpensive means of controlling fertility will be obtained.

REFERENCES

1. Pincus, G.: The control of fertility, New York, 1965, Academic Press, Inc.
2. Heller, C. G., Nelson, W. O., and Roth, A. A.: Functional prepuberal castration in males, J. Clin. Endocr. 3:573, 1943.
3. Heckel, N. J.: The influence of testosterone-tropionate upon benign prostatic hypertrophy and spermato-genesis: a clinical and pathological study in the human, J. Urol. 43:286, 1940.
4. Ross, G. T., Odell, W. D., and Rayford, P. L.: Effects of an oral contraceptive on plasma luteinizing hormone activity in women, Lancet 2:1255, 1966.
5. Swerdloff, R. S., and Odell, W. D.: Serum luteinizing and follicle stimulating hormone

levels during sequential and non-sequential contraceptive treatment of eugonadal women, J. Clin. Endocr. 29:157, 1969.

6. Mishell, D. R., and Odell, W. D.: Effect of varying dosages of ethynodiol diacetate upon serum luteinizing hormone, Amer. J. Obstet. Gynec. 109:140, 1971.

7. Odell, W. D., Parlow, A. F., Cargille, C. M., and Ross, G. T.: Radioimmunoassay for human follicle-stimulating hormone: physiological studies, J. Clin. Invest. 47:2551, 1968.

8. Corfman, P. A., and Segal, S. J.: Biologic effects of intrauterine devices (current developments: an evaluation), Amer. J. Obstet. Gynec. 100:448, 1968.

9. Intrauterine contraception, International Congress Series No. 96, Amsterdam, 1965, Excerpta Medica Foundation, Inc.

10. Intrauterine contraception, International Congress Series No. 54, Amsterdam, 1962, Excerpta Medica Foundation, Inc.

11. El Sahwi, Samir, and Moyer, Dean L.: Antifertility effects of the intrauterine foreign body, Contraception 2:1, July, 1970.

INDEX

INDEX

INDEX